David Taylor is one of the world's few independent zoo veterinary consultants. Among his clients are Royal Windsor Safari Park, Madrid Zoo, Knie's Kinderzoo, Switzerland, Trust Houses Forte Dolphinaria, Rio Leon Safari Park, Spain, Marineland Majorca, Marineland Côte d'Azur, Ouwehands Zoo, Holland, Stukenbrock Safari Park and Florida Dolphin Show, Germany, Billy Smart's Circus and Austen Brothers' Circus. He is a Fellow of the Royal College of Veterinary Surgeons and of the Zoological Society of London. He lives within a short car dash of London's Heathrow Airport with a bag constantly packed to answer emergency calls for exotic animals in places as far flung as Europe, Asia or Latin America. He frequently appears on radio and television talking about animals.

D1546313

DOCTOR IN THE ZOO

Doctor in the Zoo

The Making of a Zoo Vet

DAVID TAYLOR

With line drawings by
Frankie Coventry

London
UNWIN PAPERBACKS
Boston   Sydney

First published in Great Britain by
George Allen & Unwin 1978
First published in Unwin Paperbacks 1980

UNWIN ® PAPERBACKS
40 Museum Street, London WC1A 1LU

© David Taylor 1978, 1980

British Library Cataloguing in Publication Data

Taylor, David, b.1934
    Doctor in the Zoo.
    1. Veterinary medicine   2. Zoological gardens
    I. Title
    636.089′092′4   SF753

    ISBN 0-04-925016-7

Cover photograph by Tony Evans

Printed in Great Britain by
Hunt Barnard Printing Ltd, Aylesbury, Bucks.

Contents

To Stephanie and Lindsey

I

The Dwonikers

Fifty yards away I knew by the high-pitched bleep-bleep coming from my car that someone, somewhere, was looking for me. I unlocked, switched off the bleeper and called up the radio telephone operator.

"Call for you from Holland, Dr. Taylor," she said. "A dwoniker has escaped from an animal dealer near Utrecht. He wants you to go over straightaway with your dart-pistol to anaesthetize it. Over."

"Roger, wilco," I replied, according to protocol, and drove home wondering about the meaning of the peculiar message. "Shelagh," I called to my wife as I walked in the door, "what the dickens is a dwoniker?"

Shelagh had no more idea than I did. I called up the operator again to check the name of the beast. Yes, she was quite certain. A dwoniker was on the loose in the land of windmills. As we made our way to Manchester Airport Shelagh and I went over the possibilities concerning the identity of the mysterious animal. Brand new kinds of animal are discovered every year, and it is not all that long ago since as large and spectacular a creature as the okapi was first reported, but I thought it unlikely that the dealer had stumbled across a completely new species. Assuming I was right, the dwoniker might be a beast that I had never heard of, the name of something that had been mangled in the process of transmission by phone from Holland to England, or the Dutch name for something mundane like a deer or a llama. I plumped for the last alternative. "It's a typically Dutch word," I stated confidently. "Bet it's a rhinoceros gone berserk." Although "dwoniker" did indeed have the ring of a Dutch word, my knowledge of the language was in fact limited to the three words for "yes", "no" and an unmentionable part of one's anatomy.

Shelagh was convinced that the answer lay in the name being scrambled by the telephone operators. "Think of some animals' names that are similar to 'dwoniker'," she advised, "something that sounds roughly like it." We tried, but the best we came up with was duiker, the English name coming from the Dutch for a genus of small African antelopes.

The more I thought about it, the more I came round to the idea that duiker was right. But if one of those fleet-footed, minuscule creatures had done a bunk, it would be incredibly difficult to pursue it, stalk it and fire an anaesthetic dart successfully at it in open countryside, even assuming I could find it in the first place. I had chased escaped red deer, ten times the size of duiker, enough times and been lucky to get a momentary glimpse of them after hours of searching. Nor did I know much about duiker. I had seen them at London Zoo but most other collections in Britain did not exhibit them. This would be my first encounter with one: that was about all I knew. I hoped that these small, frail and probably highly expensive individuals would agree with my anaesthetics if I was lucky enough to get within darting range. God forbid that they should be one of that "awkward squad" among antelopes for whom certain knock-out chemicals paralyse the heat-control centre in the brain so that the unconscious creature suffers a rocketing rise in temperature that can easily and fatally cook the vital central nervous system.

At Amsterdam's Schiphol Airport the animal dealer, Mr. van den Baars, was waiting. As we walked to his car I forgot that the real identity of the "dwoniker" still hung in the air. "Where is the duiker, exactly?" I asked.

"Duiker, what duiker? Oh, do you mean dike?" said van den Baars, slightly puzzled.

"The duiker, the one that's escaped."

The Dutchman laughed. "I really don't know where you got that from. My duiker are all safely tucked up. No, the problem is with two onagers that have slipped out of my quarantine farm."

Onagers! Two onagers. "Dwonikers". Listening to the dealer's rapid, accented English, I understood how the radio telephone operator might easily have created a mythical beast. At last I had the solution to the mystery and knew my quarry: a couple of onagers, the rare and valuable wild asses of Central Asia which always reminded me of sandy-coloured and rather unspectacular mules.

"They've been sighted on a water meadow about a mile from the farm," said my companion. "It's open country and they're grazing quietly, or at least they were."

We swept along the motorway past the neat, dull townships outside Amsterdam with the evening sun flashing off the black water of the narrow canals that ran everywhere. Onagers were also a new species for me, but they were nice-sized members of the equine family. I had doped a good number of horses and zebras and even the odd Przevalski's horse, another wild species. I was carrying drugs which could be used safely on all the equines, although some needed comparatively bigger doses, pound for pound, than others.

Mr. van den Baars stopped the car in a narrow lane and pointed across a low hedge. At first all I could see were acres and acres of green grass in one gigantic field. Then I spotted the onagers. They were right in the middle, looking like two creamy-coloured mice from where we sat and cropping happily at the lush pasture in the golden light. "There they are," said the Dutchman, "and here come Piet and Kees with crates on the tractor. I'll stay here in the car. What do you plan to do?"

I squinted into the distance. There was no cover anywhere near the onagers. I would have to try the disarming, non-chalant approach. "I'll go alone to see if I can dart the pair," I said. "Keep your men back here till I wave. Then send them over. Shouldn't be much problem, if I can get within forty feet. But if they start to run. . . ." I shook my head. With night coming on and so much room to manoeuvre, the onagers could stay out of range until I had to give up. I wished I had a dart-rifle, for in that vast field my pistol seemed about as potent as a peashooter.

Loading two darts with anaesthetic, I climbed over a gate in the hedge and ran down a bank onto the billiard-table surface of the meadow. I marched off towards my prey, cocking the pistol, screwing the gas-control knob to maximum pressure and keeping one finger on the safety catch. The sun was an orange semicircle on the horizon. I realized that I was working several feet below sea level. As I came nearer to the grazing onagers one of them looked up, munching, pricked its ears and alerted the other. From 250 yards away they stared at me. Now for my display of cunning, a simple device which I had found effective three times out of ten and idiotically useless the other seven. It relies on my ability to impersonate a harmless rustic out for an evening stroll with nothing but innocent thoughts in his head. The yokel ambles along and pays not the slightest attention to the odd hippopotamus or aardvark—or onager—that might cross his path. So bucolic a fellow, gazing at the sky, humming to himself, is the very opposite of the predatory human, the pursuing keeper or beady-eyed veterinarian, whom such creatures can spot from a mile away. It is essential when using this ploy not to approach the animals head on. I shuffle along on a course which will take me at an angle across their bows and not too close to them.

This is what I did as I came closer to the onagers. My dart-gun was hidden in my arms folded idly across my chest. I seemed, I hoped, to be deep in thought, thought far removed from onager hunting, as I flicked at the occasional tussock of grass with my toe, watched birds fly by and sang a low, gentle song. Having taken a furtive glance at the onagers to establish their position, I gazed steadfastly at everything else and studiously avoided being seen looking at them. I was quite pleased with my performance. "Dum de dum dum," I carolled softly. I was reducing the distance slowly but steadily. I picked a stem of grass and chewed it like rustics are said to do. Great acting—I reminded myself of the young Olivier. "Dum de dum dum." It must have been plain that if there was one thing I was not interested in, that thing was wild asses. "Dum de dum—aaagh!" With a great splash, the rustic found himself up to his knees in water and sinking deeper as his shoes hit mud. I had wandered into a narrow, straight-sided dike running across the meadow with banks so close together that it was almost impossible to see from twenty yards. Dripping, I struggled out and looked around. The onagers were still standing peacefully, eating and keeping an eye on me as I tried with one hand to wring some water out of my trouser legs. Yes, they must have been thinking, that's the village idiot for sure. They shook their heads and chewed on.

I resumed my quiet ramble but kept a sharp eye open for more dikes and ditches. I found them. It became apparent that the whole area was neatly subdivided by water channels in place of fences or hedges, and each time I discovered one I was almost on top of it. The harmless peasant had to do some jumping, but I was getting almost within range of my quarry. Eventually I judged I could risk standing still and glancing out of the corner of my eye at the two onagers. They were watching me but were obviously not alarmed. The range was thirty-five feet, I guessed. Close enough. I released the safety catch, followed the flight of a heron against the sky, let my face turn slowly with the bird until I was looking at the onagers, and unfolded my arms. Humming disarmingly, I took aim down the barrel of the pistol and pulled the trigger. Plop! A dart embedded itself in the plump haunch of one of the animals. Swishing its tail, it trotted off a few paces and looked round at its flank. By then I had turned my back on the onagers, apparently unconcerned but in fact hurriedly loading my second dart. Slowly I turned again.

The second onager was staring at me uncertainly, ready to beat it at the first inkling that I was up to any skulduggery. It watched me bring the pistol up, sensed danger but made its move to wheel and flee too late. A red-tasselled dart thwacked into its shoulder muscle.

Both animals were injected and should be unconscious within five minutes. I waved furiously towards the road where van de Baars and his helpers waited. By the time they arrived, the onagers should be ready for the crates. Once they were loaded, all I would have to do would be to reverse the anaesthetic with a stimulant antidote and my work would be done. The onagers began to stagger and to trot round with the peculiar high-stepping gait that equines show when an anaesthetic begins to make the world spin before their eyes. Then, suddenly, they did what so many animals do when darted with potent anaesthetics—they went straight for the nearest hazard. Be it zebra, deer, antelope or domestic horse, if there is barbed wire or a rocky hole or a marsh or a pool of water in the vicinity, a half-doped creature seems more often than not to be uncannily drawn towards it.

The two onagers high-stepped their way towards the nearest canal. With a frantic dash I managed to catch up with the closer of the two and grabbed its tail to try to brake its progress. No use. The onager blindly pulled me along behind it. I tried hauling the tail to one side to steer it away from trouble, but the wild ass was too powerful for me. With a great eruption of green water, my onager plunged into the canal. Seconds later its mate did the same twenty yards away. Now I had two expensive and rare creatures about to lose consciousness in five feet of water. Both seemed likely to drown.

I looked desperately towards the road. Van den Baars's men were just driving the tractor with the crates through the field gate towards the narrow, grassy bridge across the first dike. "Come on, schnell, schnell!" I shouted, hoping that they understood German and could hear me at that distance over the roar of their engine. The head of one of the onagers, eyes glazing, rested against the muddy side of the canal. The other was repeatedly dunking its muzzle. It was almost fully unconscious. There was only one thing to do. I jumped into the canal alongside it and grabbed the heavy head. Slithering frantically on the soft mud bottom, I tried to hold my balance and keep the nostrils above water as the onager pitched all its weight onto me. Straining, I pulled myself from under the animal and tugged its muzzle until the tip of it just rested on the bank. The other onager was going under. I dragged myself like a dishcloth out of the water, squelched quickly along the grass and then leapt into the canal again to grasp the second beast's head. "Schnell, schnell!" I kept yelling.

After what seemed like years, the men arrived, jumped off the tractor and dashed over to me. "Get the boxes off the tractor, quick!" I gasped. "I can't hold the head up much longer." I was going to have to reverse the anaesthetic with the animals still in the water. The three of us could not lift the heavy, unconscious onagers bodily out of the vertically sided waterway, but if I could bring them round enough to help themselves, maybe between their efforts and ours we could get them out and box them before they were awake enough to disappear over the horizon and start the hunt all over again. Underwater I fished in my pockets for plastic syringe, needle and antidote. There was no hope of sterilizing or disinfecting anything. The two asses and I were all covered in slimy water from top to toe.

Getting my head under the space between the lower jawbones of the onager, I managed to support the animal's head painfully on top of mine, thus freeing both my hands to load the syringe. That done, I punched a clenched fist into the base of its neck somewhere under the canal surface and raised the jugular vein where it emerged from the water. A minute after I had inserted the needle and pressed the antidote in fast, I felt power returning to the onager's muscles.

It lifted its head unaided. Looking quickly to see that its mate was still breathing above water, I told the men the next step. "I'll go under, grab one foreleg at a time, bring them up and shove them on the canal bank. Then you position the forefeet and haul on the neck. With me behind and the animal getting thrust back in its hind end, it should clamber out."

They nodded. I dived under the cold water; up to that moment I had not noticed how chilled I was. Groping blindly under the stocky body of the wild ass, I found a foreleg and hauled it up to the surface. The men reached down to help. I repeated the procedure, then waded round to the onager's rear. Slapping it on the rump and hauling its tail forward, I encouraged it to move. The drug was now almost completely reversed. With a great heave, the beast lunged over the edge of the canal, the men clung onto its neck, and before it could fully regain its senses it was bundled into one of the waiting crates.

I refilled my syringe and for the fourth time that day did my impersonation of a cumbersome water sprite by jumping into the water by the second onager. We went through the same routine. The reviving animal scrambled out and was pulled towards the crate. This time, as it went over the edge of the canal with me manipulating the tail, it lashed out smartly with one of its hind legs. The unshod but solid hoof caught me squarely on the chest and I crashed backwards under the water for yet another thorough immersion. Picking myself up from the mud beneath the water, I wondered momentarily what on earth had made me choose a life which led to floundering in the depths of a Dutch canal with water weed over my eyes and up my nostrils.

When both onagers were safely restored to the quarantine farm I darted them again, this time with long-acting penicillin, for fear that my insanitary injections in the canal might have introduced germs along with the needle.

"Now, Dr. Taylor," said van den Baars as I stood shivering in my underpants and put on my spare clothes, "perhaps you would like to warm up with a glass or two of our good Holland gin. You've certainly earned it. I must thank you most sincerely—on behalf of the dwonikers."

2

Grandmother

The first steps along the road to that muddy Dutch dike were taken as a young schoolboy with an absorbing interest in everything which flew, swam, crept or crawled. Wandering the fields and moors of the Pennines around my home in Rochdale, near Manchester, I would find no end of creatures obviously in trouble, especially sheep. Unable to rise, often with inflamed and swollen vulvas, frequently being eaten away by blowfly maggots, these pitiful animals lay alone on windswept hillsides or at the bottom of quarries, or struggled in moorland streams. It was no use trying to find the owners of the sheep. The moors are vast and the flocks wander for miles, gathered in only once or twice a year by shepherds who miraculously know where they are likely to be. Besides, the farmers did not bother to do anything for these fallen individuals even when they came across one. "'Twon't do no good, lad," they would say, turning their back on the animal's misery and trudging off. The moor was common land and the grass free food. Losing a few sheep from disease or foxes or thieves was part of the game. They still made enough to live by.

School homework would be forgotten as I crouched in the rain over yet another sodden woolly body, thumbing through a book called *Veterinary Counter Practice*. This slim volume was written to help chemists give first-aid advice in their shops to pet owners. It was illustrated by Edwardian engravings of bearded men in frock coats solemnly holding unprotesting and improbable cats with linen-draped heads over bowls belching medicated steam, and of ornately coiffed ladies using what looked like armoured gauntlets to thrust pills down dogs' throats. Certainly it was the Gospel on veterinary matters as far as I was concerned. I did not know that I was looking at sheep dying of gas-gangrene brought on by difficult lambing, with livers riddled with fluke parasites or with bloodstreams lethally deficient in calcium, none of which was mentioned in my book. I just covered the animals with my jacket, treated their inflamed parts with Germolene ointment, picked the maggots off them and forced Dad's brandy between their lips.

I do not think a single one of my sheep patients ever recovered. Once, twice, sometimes three times a day I would go out to them and sooner or later I would find them dead. On one black occasion I came across a ram that had fallen into a quarry but was still alive. The jagged ends of its shattered femur poked a full four inches through the skin, alive with industrious bluebottles. Trembling and sick with fright, I killed my first patient, suffocating him with my jacket wrapped tight round his nostrils and mouth. He took a long time to die. I walked home dizzy with remorse and did not sleep at all for two nights.

In addition to the Germolene and brandy, my box of medicaments included vitamin tonic and tincture of arnica, a stinging brown herbal preparation which was my grandmother's cure-all. Grandmother seldom walked out on the moors with me, but was my ally, mentor, co-conspirator and assistant in all my surgical work at home on small beasts. She was a spirited, bustling woman with features the colour of pale honey and homely as an oven-bottom muffin. She knew alcohol, tobacco and cosmetics to be works of the Devil and had stormed out of church in mid-sermon when the new curate had revealed himself to be an evolutionist. Sturdily built, with grey gleaming eyes in a round face, she ate little other than a sort of unbleached tripe, a diet which she never appeared to find monotonous and which she augmented on Mondays with cold fatty mutton and mint sauce. The small boys of the neighbourhood held her in great respect for the way in which, if she were so minded, she could strike a brilliant shower of sparks from the cobblestones in our back street by clipping them expertly with her iron-soled Lancashire clogs. Lots of the lads, myself included, could kick atoms of fire from the stones like this as we lounged outside on a summer evening, but none of us could approach the effortless pyrotechnic display put on by the old lady as she passed us on her way to or from the tripe shop.

There was a second reason why the small boys held her in great awe. Along with the strictly seasonal hobbies of "swaling" (burning the dead grass on the moor edges), "conkering" (duelling with horse chestnuts hardened and threaded onto pieces of string in which the object was to split one's opponent's nut away from its string), cricket, and whipping tops along the flagstones, we all kept mice. The problem was that getting hold of tame mice was almost impossible during the war years, and there was a serious dearth of the small rodents in the hutches, pockets and private hideaways of the boys in our street. Grandmother solved the problem. Somehow she found out that they kept mice, both white and chocolate coloured, at the Rochdale gas-works, presumably to test for gas just as canaries were used in coal mines. One Saturday morning she led a band of us down to the gasworks. We each carried some form of small container, a tin or a cardboard box. Ecstatically, we came home with mice; Grandmother knew the man who had the key to the room where the mice were kept. Normally a surly individual, he was genial in Grandmother's presence and chuckled as he put one or two of the velvety little creatures into each of the containers thrust urgently under his nose. After that breakthrough, we tried visits to the gasworks alone, but without Grandmother it never worked. They had none to spare, they did not keep any mice, the man was too busy. But for Grandmother, persuaded by a gaggle of imploring six- and seven-year-olds to make a detour from her Saturday trip to market, mice were always forthcoming.

Hardworking and practical, she was at the same time highly sentimental. She paid me threepence a week to sing for her each Sunday evening a sugary ballad entitled "I'll Walk Beside You" while my mother accompanied me on the piano. This excruciating ritual regularly brought tears to Grandmother's eyes (and had the same effect, though for different reasons, on the rest of the household); mercifully it ceased when my voice began to change.

In her youth Grandmother had been a seamstress, and she insisted that I learn to sew and knit, arguing that the art of surgery on which my heart was firmly set was just cutting and stitching, and that neatness in weaving threads in and out of living flesh could be developed on pieces of flannel, silk and worsted. I spent hours grafting squares of cloth together under Grandmother's grey, hawk-like eyes and had my knuckles painfully rapped by one of her thick metal knitting needles whenever I grew careless. Her wisdom was confirmed years later at university when the Surgery Professor, watching the students clumsily practise their first simple operations on the chill, unbleeding bodies of already dead animals, urged us to darn our socks and sew on buttons at every opportunity. "Less beer and wenching and more needlework, gentlemen," he would roar as we cobbled away at the corpses.

Grandmother and I made a good team. She was adept with the only anaesthetic we had, a freezing spray of ethyl chloride. With one hand she would hold the struggling form of a thrush I had found fluttering and tumbling frantically through the undergrowth, and with the other would direct a stream of the numbing liquid onto the bird's shattered wing bone. As hoarfrost formed on the bloodstained flight feathers, she would tell me to begin splinting the limb with matchsticks and strips of sticking-plaster, her eyes following the movements of my fingers through a pair of gold-rimmed spectacles.

My parents tolerated well enough at first the toads convalescing in the bathroom cupboard, the paralysed owl that sat on top of the grandfather clock in the hall and the rabbit road-accident victims that either regained vitality or inexorably wasted away in the emergency wards I established in empty zinc washing tubs. But as the number of patients grew, so did the problems. The owl on the hall clock stopped the ancient timepiece when I forgot one day to replace the sheet of newspaper on which he squatted and his droppings slipped through a gap in the wooden casing and completely clogged the brass works. With the greatest difficulty Dad cleaned them up, but the clock never worked properly again. Still, if any member of the family raised the matter of the luckless clock, Grandmother would fold her arms, heave up her bosom and tetchily remind all present that it was her clock, that it suited her very well and that it never had kept good time: a preposterous statement that all knew, but none dared say, was the very opposite of the truth. With the grumblings silenced, Grandmother would slip me a solemn wink.

When the war came, our house's old coal-cellar was converted into the family's air-raid shelter. Its ceiling was reinforced by bracing beams and pillars, and bunk beds and supplies of tinned food were put in there. In fact, Rochdale was never attacked and the family did not seem to make use of the shelter during the infrequent air-raid warnings. I soon saw how this could be turned to my advantage, for there had been more trouble with my parents over my veterinary activities. My father, going into the garden to inspect the rows of glass cloches under which he grew radishes and lettuce, had found not only that his ripe, fresh salad had been requisitioned for essential victualling of the rabbit wounded in the zinc tubs, but also that two recuperating old hedgehogs were actually bedded down within the line of cloches.

Grandmother to the rescue again. She stood between my irate father and myself and defended her beloved seven-year-old grandson. "Enough of that, Frank," she said to my father, wagging a stern finger. "There's a war on, you know."

That was all she said. The power was in the way she said it. I can still remember clearly the sheer force of her words as she stood, arms akimbo, grey eyes unblinking. Nothing could have sounded less unreasonable or more obvious: with a war on it was time for every English man and woman, and every English rabbit, owl and hedgehog, to stand shoulder to shoulder in the common cause.

Next day, as Grandmother replanted Dad's garden with salad seeds, I took her into my confidence and outlined my idea of putting the more contentious species of mammal and bird in the apparently unused air-raid shelter.

"Your mum won't have it, dear," Grandmother murmured as we discussed the possibilities. "I know we don't often use the shelter, but suppose we do, some time?"

I argued that it was most unlikely that we would and that, apart from the old lavatory in the yard, I had no alternatives. Grandmother eventually agreed to help me but suggested that I bring my patients into the room via the chute which had been the means of delivering coal from the street when the coal-cellar was being used for its original purpose. In this way I would avoid the front and back doors and the attentions of other members of the family. It was a sound idea. My accomplice waited in the big room next door to the coal-cellar, bottling fruit, squeezing clothes through the mangle in front of the high open coal fire or doing a bit of whitewashing. With my patient in a sack or wrapped in my jacket I lifted the heavy iron grate from the coal chute at pavement level and slid down into the new hospital ward. There on the bunk beds I had the boxes, tins, jars and cages that held the sick and infirm. When the coast was clear, Grandmother would slip in and we would get to work.

The air-raid shelter hospital survived a first discovery by my young sister, Vivienne, who stumbled on it one day but was bought off by Grandmother, who gave Vivienne a little locket in exchange for her silence. Shortly afterwards, however, an air raid over Manchester led to Rochdale having a long alarm call on the sirens. The sound of bombing could be distinctly heard in our house that night and my parents decided we should all sleep in the shelter. Piling through the doorway in their pyjamas, the family found the place of refuge already fully occupied by things furry, scaly and feathered. Worse, my father discovered that I had used almost the whole cache of tinned corned beef on feeding the hedgehogs, and my little sister was bitten through her night-dress as she sleepily sat down on the bottom bunk and on the orphan fox cub to whom it belonged.

Grandmother miraculously soothed everyone's shattered nerves and fearlessly admitted opening the tins of corned beef for me, but then and there my long-suffering father decided to convert the lavatory in the yard into a recognized and approved wild animal hospital. The problem with the lavatory/hospital was that there was no room for Grandmother and me to do any actual work. That still had to be done elsewhere. Our favourite place was the kitchen. The light was good and that was essential, particularly for our regular hedgehog clinics. Together we would set about painting with chloroform the bloated blood-sucking ticks clinging to the bellies of our prickly patients. After waiting a few moments for a parasite to loosen its hold, Grandmother would stand back while I, as head surgeon, picked it off with tweezers. The trouble with hedgehogs, particularly sick ones, is that they often carry a hefty load of fleas around with them as well. The warm kitchen seemed to encourage these prodigious jumpers to leave their hosts, and on one potentially disastrous occasion my mother found scores of energetic little varmints leaping about on some pastry she was rolling out. Grandmother seized one, cracked it between finger and thumbnail and pronounced it to be a mosquito. Since it was late January, she had to add that it was an unseasonably early mosquito, but after that we began to use DDT powder on the animals before putting them into the hospital shed. Grandmother always made sure my mother was out or busy somewhere else in the house before we began hedgehog clinics. We used the kitchen table and spoke in low voices.

When things went well, Grandmother would hum gleefully and give me a hug. Just having me to herself pleased her enormously and, although she undoubtedly loved the animals we dealt with, her principal reward I think was to feel that in some way she was helping to lay the first tiny foundations of what we both wanted me to become—a veterinarian. We would never dream that I might do anything else or that I might not be able to qualify for veterinary school. "Why," Grandmother would tell her cronies, "one day David's going to treat tigers." She was dead right.

When it came to goldfish, newts and frogs with skin diseases we at first did not do very well. I painted their ulcers with creams and antiseptic lotions but the water quickly washed these away. Time after time I had to bury my failures in the garden.

"I've an idea," Grandmother said one day, as she watched me dispose of the most recent victim, a goldfish. "Go and get me the paste I use for my false teeth, David!"

I went upstairs for the ointment that Grandmother, locked in the bathroom, used in the mysterious ritual of her toilet each morning.

"Now," she said when I gave her the tin of tacky grey stuff, "next time we have a goldfish with one of those nasty sores, we'll paint on the arnica as usual but then, before putting him back in the water, we'll smear on some of this denture paste. It's funny stuff; as soon as it gets wet it sets like wax. That's how I keep my teeth in, young feller. Here— try a bit."

I took a little of the grey paste and put it on my tongue.

It was tasteless but I could feel it changing its consistency and sticking tight. I ran my tongue along the top of my mouth but the paste did not come off, and it was still hanging around when I went to bed that night. When I found the paste still unpleasantly tacky on my gums the following morning I began to realize the possibilities of the stuff. Now all we needed was a suitable case.

Some weeks later a friend brought me a lovely big frog. He was green, glistening and impassive as he sat on the palm of my hand, gulping. One of his front toes was swollen and had a parboiled appearance. Serum oozed through the skin. I showed him to Grandmother. "The false-teeth stuff," I reminded her. "This is our chance."

Grandmother was enthusiastic. "Get the paste from my room," she instructed. "We'll put it on over some comfrey ointment."

Comfrey ointment was only one of the herbal preparations whose virtues Grandmother preached. As well as arnica tincture, she taught me how to use quinine, senna and ipecacuanha wine. I was supervised in applying iodine and gentian violet and sticky kaolin poultices. Sometimes we would take animals with respiratory troubles and go out to seek the municipal road-menders with their smoking tar-boilers. Grandmother would tip the wide-eyed workmen a shilling as we stood letting an armful of sniffling hedgehog breathe in the pungent vapour for a quarter of an hour. "What's good for whooping cough in children will be good for hedgehogs," she would say confidently.

Grandmother held the frog gently while I smeared soothing, dark-green comfrey ointment on the inflamed toe. Then I covered the whole of the delicate foot with the false-teeth paste and placed the frog in a large glass jar with a couple of inches of water and a stone to climb on. I was pleased to see the paste stick to his foot as he paddled about. Next day it was still holding the comfrey ointment in place. Grandmother seemed very pleased and patted my head.

Three days later we wiped away the paste and the ointment and looked at the toe. There was no doubt about it; the swelling was going down and the toe looked healthier. I repeated the double application, returned the frog to his ward and presented him with half a dozen fat bluebottles that I had caught for him. The frog and Grandmother made veterinary history, for the toe healed completely in a week, a record for frogs attending my clinic, and we released him in the pond of a nearby park. I still use Grandmother's denture paste on dolphin and sea-lion wounds.

Grandmother also hit on a novel way of treating tortoises and similar creatures that had taken a tumble or received blows hard enough to crack their shells, exposing the soft tissues underneath. Nowadays I happily cut away great windows in tortoise and terrapin shells to do operations; the window in the shell is repaired with modern epoxy resins and glass fibre and heals perfectly in a few months. When Grandmother and I were in practice, we had no such thing as epoxy resins and plastics, but she was on the right track. I must have been about twelve years old when she came up with the notion.

"It occurs to me," she said one day when we were surveying the septic, irregular hole in a terrapin carapace caused by the bite of a cat, "that to protect the soft stuff underneath once you've cleaned it up, we should seal the hole in the shell properly. Get the Bulldog kit."

My Bulldog kit for repairing punctures in the tyres of my bicycle consisted of a small tin containing sandpaper, glue, french chalk powder and discs of inner-tube rubber. I fetched it. Inner tubes, fine, I thought as I returned with the kit, but terrapins?

But there was no arguing with Grandmother. "Now, my boy," she said, "cut out the diseased flesh." She sprayed a fine stream of freezer on the spot. "Dab on the arnica." I did as she directed. "And now go ahead as if the terrapin was just an ordinary tyre puncture."

The terrapin pulled in his head with a faint hiss, apparently resigned to reincarnation as a bicycle. I sandpapered the edges of the hole in the shell, dusted them lightly with the chalk, applied the sticky glue and pressed on a rubber patch of the appropriate size. A perfect job.

Grandmother beamed. "Now," she said, "judging by the size of the hole and knowing how long it takes one's fingernails to grow half an inch and allowing for the fact that terrapins are cold-blooded and likely to heal slower than mammals like us, I reckon you ought to be able to take a peek in about a month."

The punctured terrapin, with the black patch looking like a trapdoor covering his machinery, re-extended his head and legs when he was certain that he was back in his vivarium and not likely to find himself caught up in the Tour de France. He looked unconcerned and began nibbling a tiny pond snail.

The patch held underwater, and each day I checked the edges to see they were secure. As the days went by, "Black Spot" seemed destined to be a good deal luckier than the name I had given him. One month to the day I brought the terrapin into the kitchen. Even Grandmother held her breath as I snipped the rubber patch with her nail scissors. I peeled the rubber back and we bumped our heads as we bent for a closer look. I let out a gasp of delight; the shell had knitted together completely and healthy new carapace covered the hole. "Black Spot" did not allow himself to get excited as Grandmother and I hugged one another and laughed with relief—we took our work very seriously and shared our occasional successes with no less intimacy than when we commiserated with one another over our frequent failures.

"Grandma," I said, "one day they'll award you the Nobel Prize for Medicine."

I had total faith in Grandmother's knowledge, and only slowly did this state of affairs reverse itself. By the time I went to university she was laid low with chronic heart disease and would not take a pill or a drop of medicine prescribed by the most eminent of specialists until her grandson and one-time partner had given the OK. She was immensely proud when I made it as a veterinarian. She hung my degree scroll above her bed and lived for me to go and talk about the old days and check the latest advice of her doctor.

Some years later I tackled my first giant tortoise case, one of the massive and rare 300-pound Galapagos tortoises at Belle Vue Zoo, Manchester. Not having had experience of the immense contractile power of their hind-leg muscles, I had let the beast trap my hand securely within the shell where I had been injecting into the soft skin of the groin. I wonder what Grandmother would have to say about patching up monsters like this, I was thinking as the keepers dragged on the rapidly disappearing leg that was pinioning me. I would tell her about it when I visited her that evening, now bed-ridden but alert as ever. I could imagine her softly wrinkled golden face breaking into a wide grin as I reminded her about "Black Spot" and compared him with his huge Galapagos relative.

The telephone rang. The head reptile keeper took the call and then came over to me.

"Dr. Taylor," he said, "bad news, I'm afraid. Your father rang to say that your grandmother has just passed away."

3
Red-letter Wednesday

Thanks to Grandmother's encouragement, my passion for animals stayed with me through school and university, and at university I found myself being drawn more and more towards the care of the exotic species, the wild, sometimes rare animals who, it seemed to me, demanded veterinary work of the most challenging and the most rewarding sort. After graduating in the late 'fifties I took a partnership in a veterinary practice in my home town of Rochdale, Lancashire. Rochdale is a grey, lustreless town of around 100,000 souls lying beneath the damp western slopes of the desolate and rocky Pennine moorland, with the big industrial centre of Manchester situated on the flat land twelve miles to the west and surrounded by smaller towns and villages, all of which saw their heyday in the industrial revolution and the reign of King Cotton, when the moist climate of Lancashire was so perfect for the spinning of yarn before air-conditioning and humidifiers were dreamed of. Above Rochdale's cobbled streets rose a forest of tall mill chimneys, but what sorts of animals were to be found in those drizzly streets, in the shabby smallholdings and on the bleak, windy moorlands? Certainly none of the wild, exciting creatures of which I dreamed: tigers, buffaloes or armadilloes.

A typical veterinary practice in Rochdale consisted of a mixture of household pets and farm animals, and it was on dogs involved in road accidents, sows that got into difficulties when giving birth and sheep struck down by mysterious lethal epidemics that I learned the arts of surgery, obstetrics and medicine. It was useful, rewarding experience in a general practice like hundreds of others in the north of England—but there was something else, something of vital importance to a young vet who had already developed a consuming interest in exotic species. Among the clients of the practice I had joined was the large zoo in Manchester, Belle Vue. There were other practices nearer the zoo but the connection went back to the nineteenth century, when Rochdale was the veterinary centre of that part of England. The vet in the practice who had for several years done all the work at Belle Vue was Norman Whittle, and with him I had visited cases at the zoo as a student and had first gained some idea of the problems of exotic animal medicine. Now that I was qualified, surely I could achieve my ambition and get to grips myself with the diseases of the wild animals in the zoo in Manchester. But how? The zoo director had a good working relationship with Norman Whittle and trusted him. If an elephant was sick or a python poorly, it was Whittle he sent for. What possible good could Taylor, the new boy, do? There was apparently no escape from my predicament. I could not get in to do the work because my experience was virtually nil, but unless I did achieve a breakthrough and treated some zoo animals I could not begin to get the experience.

Wednesdays began to assume an immense importance in my life, for Norman had his half-day off each week on Wednesday afternoon and I was on call for Belle Vue. This might be my chance, I thought, but for months I was disappointed. Unless the zoo needed him urgently they would leave a message asking Norman to call on the Thursday morning, and in the rare event of an emergency, Edith, our receptionist, would manage to contact him wherever he was and that was the end of his half-day relaxation. It was most frustrating; my one chance to deputize for my senior partner was if he was out of contact on a Wednesday afternoon or away, on holiday abroad for instance, but on these occasions Belle Vue's animal stock seemed to be strictly on their best behaviour and paragons of blooming health and vitality, right down to the weediest chipmunk in the small mammal house.

Then it happened. It was Wednesday afternoon. Norman Whittle had gone to the coast and was not expected back until late. The zoo director, Mr. Wilson, rang. Edith explained that Norman was away. Yes, OK then, was the reply, if it had to be Dr. Taylor, Dr. Taylor it would have to be. But hurry! One of the chimpanzees had lost a thumb. I jumped gleefully into my battered old Jowett van and set off.

It had all started over the asparagus. Each day a rich variety of fruits and vegetables was sent up to the great ape house at Belle Vue from the wholesale market in the city, depending on price, availability and what was in season. Out of the day's selection Len, the senior ape keeper, would build up a balanced and attractive diet for his collection of chimps, orang-utans and gorillas. A slim, phlegmatic individual with grey eyes blinking behind spectacles and a chirpy Manchester accent, he had to make sure that the apes received essential protein, vitamins and roughage. Whenever possible he included delicacies which his charges could enjoy for the sheer fun of eating—grapes, pomegranates or peaches. An odd case of eggplants or avocados left unsold at the end of the day would usually end up at the zoo, and on this particular day a crate stuffed with tender asparagus bunches had arrived. Len took a few bunches down to the ape house to see what his chimps would make of them.

Robert, the big male chimpanzee, shared quarters with two adoring females, Sapphire and Chloe. Robert was a highly successful chimp Casanova who had sired a number of healthy infants at Belle Vue. As his reputation for a reliable, no-nonsense approach to the business of breeding grew, he acted as surrogate husband to a number of females sent in from other zoos. Whether they were ugly or pretty, placid or

3

cantankerous, intelligent or somewhat simple-minded, it did not matter to Robert. He accepted all comers with equal decorum, and the erstwhile barren females would leave after a few weeks' amorous holiday in Manchester, indubitably and uncomplainingly pregnant. As well as being a most gallant and gentle begetter, though, Robert was also a gourmand; in fact he was downright greedy. Woe betide anybody who came between him and his victuals. If he fancied something tasty he had to have it, and none of his companions dared indicate that perhaps Robert's eyes were too big for his belly.

When Len gave a bunch of the tender white and lilac asparagus shoots to each of the three chimps who stuck their arms through the bars, it was the first time that any of them had seen this vegetable. Robert shuffled through his bundle of succulent stalks, sniffed the buds, took a bite and found them exquisite. Sapphire and Chloe were doing the same. Robert gulped down his share and craved a second helping. Sapphire's had all gone but Chloe still held a few pieces; like Gladstone, she believed in the virtue of thoroughly chewing her food. Grunting, Robert shuffled over to Chloe and imperiously thrust a hairy hand towards the remaining asparagus stalks. Chloe whipped them smartly behind her back and screeched at the importunate male, her lips curled back and her white teeth chattering. For a second or two Robert was nonplussed—he was used to getting his own way without resistance. He put on one of his menacing looks and pushed his face close to Chloe's. Eyeball to eyeball, unblinking, Robert glared one of his most meaningful glares, a glare which in the past had never failed to bring mischievous adolescent chimps and timorous keepers to heel, and which had quelled many a nagging old matriarchal ape. Chloe did the unthinkable; she bit his ear, neatly punching a small but painful hole through the middle of the flap. Astounded, Robert backed off half a pace. This was too much! With a short, sharp rush he threw his 150 pounds at Chloe, bowling

her over and grabbing with both hands at the stalks she was tenaciously clutching. Struggling and screaming, she refused to let go as Robert pulled her clenched fist towards his bared teeth. His enormously strong index finger could not winkle its way into her palm, nor could his conical yellow canine teeth prize open her grip. Thwarted, Robert was driven to desperate measures, and with a single easy scrunch of his jaws he bit off Chloe's thumb; it was sliced off as cleanly as a severed stalk of celery. Chloe at once released the remains of the asparagus. Robert quickly gobbled them down, then picked up the amputated thumb, sniffed indifferently at it and threw it out of the cage in the direction of Len, who had watched the drama helplessly.

Those few sticks of asparagus resulted in Chloe being maimed for life, although she learned to make do with nine instead of ten digits in no time at all. They were also the reason why I was bouncing in the Jowett through grimy streets of small terraced houses and steaming fish-and-chip shops, on my way, alone, to my very first unaided zoo case at the age of twenty-two.

The twelve-mile drive to the zoo gave me time to think. The message had said something about a thumb being lost by a female chimp. I knew little else at that stage. Still, fingers were like toes and I had treated dozens of cases of domestic animals which had lost toes or had had to have them surgically amputated. The operation was comparatively simple. Bandaging the injured zone after treatment presented no complications, and I had long ago mastered a handful of little tricks using lacquer, sticky tape, repellent aerosol sprays, leather bootees or plastic bags to protect dressings against the teeth, claws and persistent ingenuity of indignant tabby cats and frantic poodles. Yes, I reassured myself as I wound my way through the traffic, fingers were indeed like toes.

Then the snags started to occur to me. Tabby cats and poodles, even for that matter cows, were all fairly easy to anaesthetize. There was always a fond owner or burly farmer to hold the creature while I injected the anaesthetic. Dart-guns were still years in the future. Who was going to hold the chimp? Again, my arts of wound dressing had been developed in animals which had no manual dexterity. Might not a wily ape remove whatever dressing I used in little more time than I took to put it on? It dawned on me that I did not know the best dose for chimpanzees of the one anaesthetic that I might have to use: barbiturate. At the time all my other anaesthetics were either gases like ether and halothane—and I could hardly walk up to a 150-pound great ape, slap a mask on its knowing face and ask it to count backwards from one hundred—or other injectable knock-out drugs which were old-fashioned, risky or corrosive. Barbiturate, the latest anaesthetic for veterinary use at the time, was at least safer but one needed to know something about dosage. Supposing I lost my first zoo patient! I gulped. It was a prospect too awful even to contemplate. Take it easy, I told myself, what am I worrying about? Drip it into the chimp's vein a little at a time until the desired level of sleep has been achieved. That way, providing I don't rush it, I'm bound not to exceed the safety limit.

Two miles to go. I tried not to think about the anaesthetic problem; the dripping-in method would be just the thing. But hold on a minute, the slow drip into the vein is all very well, but what is the chimp going to do during the seconds or even minutes when she begins to sense the first hint of dizziness, when she sees double or the room gently begins to spin? She's going to have ample time, if you don't knock her straight out, to part company with your carefully implanted intravenous needle and play havoc with any homo sapiens in the operating theatre—particularly the anaesthetist. Less than confident now, and for a fraction of a second cursing my stars for arranging that the thumb should take leave of its owner on a Wednesday, I swung into the zoo entrance. The commissionaire peered suspiciously through my side window and beckoned to me to wind it down.

"Yes, sir," he growled, "what can we do for you?"

I tried to shake off my apprehension and put on a professional face. "It's the vet," I replied loudly.

"You're not Dr. Whittle."

"No, but I am the vet." And then, as an afterthought—it sounded rather grand—"To see the chimpanzee, an emergency." The gates were opened and I drove into the grounds.

As I stopped the van outside the great ape house, the face of Matt Kelly, the head keeper, peered from the door. Grabbing my bag I climbed out of the van. My heart was hammering in a mixture of excitement and dread. This was it. Another face appeared at the door as I approached. It was Mr. Wilson, the zoo director. Just my luck, I thought, to have this pair of Celts to deal with on my first zoo case. I had met both of them at the zoo with Norman Whittle when I was still a student. Kelly was a tough, experienced and shrewd Irishman and Wilson an acerbic Scot with a face like a walnut. Both knew a lot about animals, were intolerant of fools and amateurs and did not seem much impressed by veterinarians in the zoo. Students, it had seemed to me, were held by both of them in some contempt, and both of them undoubtedly considered me still very much a student where exotic animals were concerned. It was true, but dammit, I had to begin somewhere. The trouble was that they knew this was my beginning, and I knew they knew. I crossed my fingers under the handle of my medical bag.

"Good afternoon, Mr. Wilson, Mr. Kelly," I began, "Dr. Whittle's away and out of contact, I'm afraid, so you've got me." I gave a rather tentative jolly laugh.

The two zoo men greeted me stonily. "Yes, well, come and have a look at Chloe," Wilson said, and led the way into a corridor flanked with a number of intricate barred gates that opened onto small cells lit solely by electric bulkhead lights. It was like walking along one of the gangways at Alcatraz. All around me the chimpanzees and orangutans set up a deafening din, screeching, rattling and beating food dishes against the walls. One big male chimp burped as I passed him and pressed his face close to the bars. I smiled at him and put out my hand to tickle one of his knuckles clenched tight round a bar.

"Careful! Don't do that!" hissed Kelly, walking behind

me. "He'll have your arm off if ye don't watch out! That's the feller that took the thumb off this afternoon."

I looked at Robert the maimer, inside for life. He gazed at me intently, eyes never blinking. As I continued on down the passageway, I felt a warm moist patch soaking through my trousers. Robert had urinated on me through the grille.

Chloe sat alone in her sleeping quarters, banging a stainless steel drinking dish on the floor with her good hand. The other, mutilated hand she held high above her head so that all the world could see the damage wrought by the evil Robert.

"That's it," said Wilson, pointing. Kelly said nothing. Both men stood looking blank. They did not seem to be anxiously awaiting my words of wisdom. I looked hard through the bars. The diagnosis was clear and simple: the thumb was off. So far so good. Now for the next stage: treatment. There were some drops of blood on the floor but the hand did not seem to be actively bleeding at present. It looked as if Robert had performed his amputation rather neatly straight through the bottom knuckle joint, so there was no surgical operation for me to do, but he had left a rather irregular edge to the skin. Ought I not to straighten that up, stitch up the hole and put a dresssing on? And was there not a risk of infection? Chimpanzee mouths normally contain a rich variety of nasty microbes, some of which can cause serious diseases when given the chance to invade healthy flesh. Yes, it looked as though I would have to do something.

I decided to broach diplomatically the subject of how to get to grips with Chloe. "Hmm," I murmured wisely and subtly. "Hmmm." I hoped the "Hmmm" was of a tone, pitch and duration perfectly calculated to suggest not that I was at a loss but rather that such cases were well within my province. Wilson and Kelly said nothing and stared blankly on.

"I see," I continued, again trying to convey optimism

and confidence rather than sterile perplexity. Still they said nothing; they were forcing me to the point where I would have to make a positive suggestion for treatment. I decided to approach the nettle obliquely before grasping it. "What's she like?" I asked. It was a suitably vague question.

Wilson frowned. "D'you mean what's she like to handle?" he snapped.

"Er, yes," I replied brightly.

"Can't," said Kelly lugubriously. "Can't."

"Well, I think we ought to stitch up the hole if we can, dress it and give her a shot of antibiotic," I went on. "What would be the best way, do you think?"

A distinctly aggravated look appeared on Wilson's walnut face. "Can't," he said. "There's no way of doing it."

I had to say my piece. "Is there no way you can hold her long enough for me to get some barbiturate into her vein?" I asked in my politest voice.

Both men broke into a burst of humourless laughter. "Catch hold of her? Chloe? Impossible. Impossible." Wilson's nae-nonsense Glasgow accent seemed stronger than ever. "How do you suggest we do that?"

The ball was back in my court. "Well, if you've no way of trapping her, and we've no way of getting a drug in by injection, the only thing is to try doping her food."

"No chance." This time it was Kelly's turn. "She's fed up for today, won't take any more. Anyway, Chloe's as sharp as they come at spottin' doctored food."

If I had to wait until the next day, and then still use the imprecise and unpredictable way of introducing barbiturate in the food, I would have lost valuable time. Infection might have set in and the stitches might not be so certain of holding. What would we have done if the animal had been haemorrhaging severely? Waited until she was so weakened by blood loss that she had no more will to resist?

I stood looking in at the wounded chimpanzee. The case was a supremely simple one, the type of therapy obvious, but there was nothing I could do. The zoo director and the head keeper knew that I would be unable to make any positive, constructive contribution; they must have known it when the call had been put through to my office. With a first personal taste of gnawing impotence, I began to realize the futility of veterinary medicine as applied to zoo animals. It seemed in those days before the invention of the dart-gun that the zoo vet had only two alternatives: to inject, dose, lance and anoint only small, relatively non-violent creatures such as lizards and turtles, whose problems were obscure, unstudied and baffling to the veterinarian familiar with the workings and ways of domestic animals; or to stand at one side of the bars and guess what might be wrong with the choleric gorilla or tiger that lay on the other side, obviously ill or injured but just as obviously an ungrabbable and ungrateful patient.

Chloe was one of the latter cases. I knew that with some animals it had been possible to immobilize them for treatment by using sheer brute force, casting nets over them and then having seven or eight of your heaviest men sit on the captive until it was almost suffocated or someone was severely bitten through a gap in the rope mesh. Even if such humane barbarity worked, the effect on animals and staff was utterly demoralizing. The end result was a terrified, exhausted patient, still virtually unexaminable. No point in taking his temperature; it was roaring up in panic. No chance of feeling with one's fingers for the liver abscess or ball of cancer that might lie in the abdomen; the body wall was held hard as iron. And even if one could get the bell end of the stethoscope into the right position without it being bitten off, the galloping heart was masking much else which might be significant. I was not going to begin by treating my first zoo case that way.

There was nothing more to be done for Chloe except to give the zoo director a broad-spectrum antibiotic which could be added to her fruit drinks for a week or so. The three of us retraced our steps. Robert was still hugging the bars of his cell closely. I looked at him as I passed, keeping close to the opposite wall of the passageway in the hope of staying out of range. Was there in his gaze the merest hint of mockery? He grimaced and stuck his tongue behind the barely parted rows of yellow teeth. "Tsk, tsk, tsk," said Robert.

The two zoo men and I went outside and stood for a moment before I climbed back into my van.

"Well, thanks anyway for coming," said Wilson.

"Yes, it should heal up without any trouble," Kelly reassured me. "Oi've seen these chimps do terrible things to one another. It's amazin' what nature can do. Healed up in no time at all. Baboons, too—wounds ye could put your hand into after fightin'. But they heal up with no bother in a couple o' weeks."

"Well, I'd like to have sutured Chloe's hand," I replied. "Perhaps one day we'll have ways of doing such things easily enough."

I still wondered why they had bothered to send for me in such a hurry in the first place, since they did not seem the slightest dismayed by my non-performance. Having just achieved my dearest ambition, my first zoo case, I found myself driving home to Rochdale in a black depression. Could it be that after all I should stick to cattle and horses?

That evening I told my wife about my uncertain debut with Chloe, Mr. Wilson and Matt Kelly. Shelagh and I had met while we were both still at school and had courted for six years while she qualified as a therapy radiographer and I carried through my veterinary studies. Her green eyes and strong determination bear witness to her Irish ancestry, and she has a deep love and understanding of animals of every kind; I had seen her move earthworms from footpaths with the concern of a devout Hindu lest they be trodden upon and injured, we had wrestled together over many a dying animal brought to our doorstep, and we had worked side by side over pregnant ewes needing Caesarians in the middle of the night when I had no anaesthetist or surgical assistant available. Her optimism was unflagging and her judgement of the right approach to animal patient and owner impeccable.

"Don't worry," she said reassuringly, "you've not lost Chloe. There will be other times. One of these days you'll show 'em! There'll be new ways of getting at these animals and then you'll get the upper hand. Men like Kelly and Wilson have been in the business all their lives. You know the problems you've had with old-fashioned Pennine farmers in the six months since you first started in practice—they didn't want the young feller with the new-fangled ways, laughed when you sterilized the skin before injecting a cow down with milk fever, wanted you to cut the tails of tuberculous cows to get out the 'worm' that was sucking the meat off the beasts' bones—you're getting over all that with time and battling on. Same with the zoos. You've got to keep reading about exotic animals, keep going if you get the chance. One good success can make all the difference."

Shelagh was right. It would be a long haul before I could ever move about the zoos with the same growing confidence in handling every kind of case, together with the right psychological approach to the owners, that I was developing in general practice. The idea of one day working solely with exotic animals seemed the most tenuous of dreams. Even Shelagh doubted whether we would ever be able to achieve that.

On the day after my first visit to Chloe, I also tackled Norman Whittle about the affair. Norman was a quiet, elegant individual ten years my senior, with a fair moustache and, if the term can be applied to animal doctors, a superb bedside manner.

"Why do they bother to call us at all when they know there is little we can do?" I asked him.

He smiled. "Quite simply to cover themselves. To cover themselves for the sake of the Board. Happens to me all the time. Something ill, they fiddle about with it as best they can for a few days until it looks as if the poor sod's going to die, then they send for the vet. If there's going to be a corpse, they've got to be able to report to the Board that 'the vet was called in but the animal expired'. As for Chloe, she wasn't likely to die, but the same principle applies. A high-value animal they can't get to grips with and so, just in case something goes wrong, or if a visitor reports the presence of a nine-fingered ape to the RSPCA, they've got to be able to say that the buck was passed to the vet."

"So what you're saying is that we're professional fall guys for the zoo?"

"Yes, essentially. OK, so we supply them with drugs they can put in the food of animals with diarrhoea and vitamin syrup for things that look out of condition or down in the mouth, but basically we go so that on the monthly reports it can read something like 'Despite veterinary treatment, x number of mammals, y number of birds and z number of reptiles cocked their toes.' "

"Don't you feel you do some good for the zoo animals, though?"

"In a few cases, yes—calving a giraffe that's in difficulties, lancing an abscess on the occasional elephant—but they're few and far between. Mostly I haven't any way of knowing what's wrong with these creatures and they, people like Matt Kelly, know I don't know. I don't think zoos in general have much time for vets."

"But they need us to rubber-stamp the losses?"

"Afraid so."

Not only was Matt Kelly right about Chloe's hand—it healed perfectly without any infection or discomfort and within three weeks the skin had closed the gap completely—but I knew that Norman's analysis of the relationship between zoos and vets was basically true as well. Perhaps it was partly the profession's fault for paying too much attention in the past exclusively to domestic animals. Not many years earlier, veterinary education had concentrated almost solely on the problems of the horse. Gradually, as the automobile seemed likely to be more than a nine-day wonder, farm animals and then later the dog and cat received a more appropriate proportion of a student's time. Even today the handling, diseases and therapy of exotic creatures are squeezed into a total of one or two hours' instruction out of a five- or six-year course in some veterinary schools. When I first treated Chloe not even that amount of tuition was available.

The more I thought about Norman's remarks the more crystal clear it seemed to me that I had to have three things if I was ever going to progress in zoo medicine. First I had to look into new ways of getting drugs accurately inside the bodies of creatures too dangerous or too nervous to be injected by hand; secondly I needed powerful, compact, safe sedatives and anaesthetics for every possible class of exotic patient; and thirdly I would have to learn everything I could from old-timers like Kelly at Belle Vue about the lore of zoocraft, about moving among and handling difficult and dangerous animals. Matt Kelly might not know the exact location of the sinuses of Rokitansky-Aschoff in a rhinoceros's liver, or the dental formula of a binturong, but he knew a hell of a lot about the care of wild creatures. I must pry some of it out of him.

4

Parrots and Pythons

For a long time after the incident of Chloe's thumb, Norman Whittle's Wednesday afternoons, vacations and odd days in bed with influenza came and went with the same monotonous absence of disease at Belle Vue. Freezing snaps accompanied by choking yellow fog on November Wednesdays never seemed to provoke the acute lung emergencies in giraffe or antelope that sent Norman dashing out in like weather on every other day of the week, and in summer the milling crowds of visitors who fed the elephants with mouldy sausage rolls, umbrellas or cigarettes, or threw contraceptives, pins or bits of glass into the monkeys' cages, seemed to be on their most civilized behaviour whenever Norman was away and unavailable to deal personally with the resulting cases of colic and acute enteritis.

There was just one source of practical experience: the trickle of wild and exotic animals that ran fitfully through my daily work with farm animals and domestic pets. Even in darkest Lancashire there were folk who preferred keeping slow lorises to Siamese cats or who had a penchant for pythons. If their pets needed medical attention, more often than not they telephoned Belle Vue Zoo, who referred them to us. It was not much compared to the experience with real zoo animals that I longed for, but it taught a callow young vet a thing or two the hard way—and sometimes more about humans than about animals.

Most numerous among my exotic patients at this time were parrots, the choleric, beady-eyed individuals that perch behind the bars of numerous pubs in Greater Manchester, sweetly and ever so gently take peanuts placed on the capacious bosoms of the landladies whom they adore and, cursing raucously, try to take the fingers off all other members of the human race who come within reach. Without

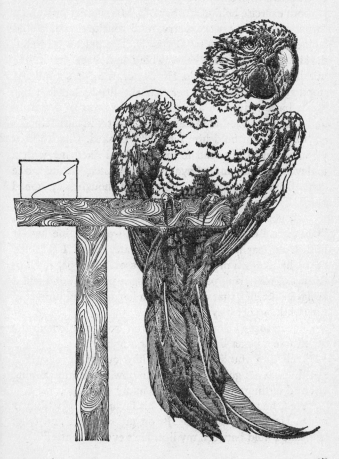

exception, these birds of glorious plumage and lengthy life-span dislike me and, as I count a fine collection of old scars on my hands, I am not sure that I am very partial to them. Parrots were small beer, I thought, but the beer soon turned distinctly sour.

Thus it was after I had been working with Norman Whittle for about a year that I met Charlie, a fine blue and gold macaw with claws overgrown as a result of twenty years without exercise behind the bar of a Manchester pub and a surfeit of fattening sweet sherry, his favourite tipple. Would I kindly trim his toenails? Certainly. The macaw glowered darkly in his carrying cage, which had been set in the middle of my surgery table. His owner, the pub's landlady, stood smiling proudly at her "cheeky little Charlie". She was a large lady with a bosom like the prow of a galleon and with peroxide-blond hair rolled tightly in curlers.

"Er, can you hold him for me?" I asked. Cheeky little Charlie turned his head to one side and fixed me with a malevolent, red-rimmed eye. A low, sinister, grating noise came from his scraggy throat and he thoughtfully honed one half of his beak against the other.

"Oh goodness, no, my dear," exclaimed the landlady. "Charlie's a darling little boy but he won't let me handle him. He'd tear me to bits. And he hates men." I reflected that I had known more promising cases. I had yet to learn the art of mastering parrots by using a piece of stick and a kung-fu-like flick that renders them harmless and unhurt in the twinkling of an eye.

Charlie rocked slowly on his perch from one foot to the other, like a boxer limbering up for a fight.

"Well, can you at least entice him out of his cage?" I asked. I was not going in to fight, so how about him coming out and settling this thing man to man?

"Well, he might come out for his favourites, after-dinner mints. He adores those. He sits on my shoulder and takes one that I hold between my lips. He's ever so gentle!"

It turned out that we had no after-dinner mints between us and I sent Edith, my receptionist, across the road to buy some; I would learn in time that a zoo vet carries a variety of delicacies in his medical bag along with the drugs and instruments; one's essential first-aid kit must include after-dinner mints for a wide variety of monkeys, parrots and small mammals, clear mints for wallabies, sugar lumps for elephants and small cheroots for aoudads and other members of the goat tribe.

"Now," said the landlady when we had the mints, "I'll put a mint between my lips, Charlie will come out, and while he's nibbling it perhaps you can clip his toes."

The macaw acted absolutely according to phase one of the plan. As soon as he spied the sweet he waddled along his perch and out of the door of the cage, and sat squarely on his owner's shoulder hard by her ear. With one golden eye he watched her place the mint between her lips and with the other he kept me under unblinking observation. Like a ventriloquist's dummy, he reached round the woman's cheek and began to nibble the mint. Slowly I sidled up and, feigning nonchalance, began to raise the clippers towards the parrot's long toenails, which were perfectly displayed against her dress just below her left shoulder. Six inches, three inches, one inch; I was getting closer to the curved talons. They certainly needed chiropody, with some grown almost to full circles. Somewhere inside them was a core of flesh with nerves and blood. I must avoid cutting into that area and simply trim back the dead, overgrown portion. But how could I tell exactly where the core of each shiny, black, opaque nail was? I would have to compromise to begin with and snip off just a little bit, see how that looked and then maybe take a sliver more.

As I reached the first claw and gingerly touched it with the tip of my clippers, Charlie kept his eye fixed firmly on me but continued to crunch at the mint without budging. Very gently I slipped the toenail clippers over the end of the first claw. Suddenly Charlie decided he had had enough. Something dastardly was afoot, and he was not going to stand by and let it happen. In order to lean forward and launch a pre-emptive attack on me and my clippers he would have to have a more secure base to perch on, so with the black claws of his left foot, Charlie dug through the landlady's dress and deeply into the flesh of her shoulder. The poor woman spat out the mint and uttered a piercing shriek that set the waiting dogs in the reception room barking and howling. A nimble tactician, Charlie was determined to bring his steely bill into close combat with the foe, but to stop himself from pressing the attack too far and too fast, with the result that he might fall off his defensive position, he needed another good secure hold for his right foot. The object he sought was right there—his owner's ear. Charlie grabbed it tightly and dug in his curly nails. The lady let out a second, more raucous shriek and clutched the parrot with both hands, whereupon he bit a plump finger and drew blood. More shrieks.

All this flurry of action had taken only a few seconds, during which time I had seemed to be transfixed, incapable of action, but now I moved forward. Impotently waving my clippers, I tried to separate the struggling mass of feathers, hair, claws and fingers on the landlady's shoulder. Scrunch, scrunch—I was painfully bitten on two fingers. Wild-eyed, ruffled and squawking, Charlie launched a new attack on my clippers. Clang! His gaping black beak punched sharply forward and knocked them from my grasp. They slipped neatly down the inside of the landlady's dress.

With the enemy now in complete disarray, Charlie was still in command of his redoubt. The ear, bright red and resembling a crushed strawberry, remained under requisition for essential military purposes, and he had given up not one inch of ground on the left shoulder. He had sacrificed a few green feathers and in the excitement of battle had elected not to desert his post to go to the latrine but to obey the call of nature just where he stood. It improved neither the lady's appearance nor her morale.

"For God's sake, can't you do something?" she yelled. "Get the little beggar off me!"

Charlie bit the back of one of her scrabbling hands. When I tried again to grab him he reinforced his hold on ear and shoulder, whisked his beak to and fro and deftly removed a piece of nail from my left index finger.

I looked desperately round for something to help me. A towel hung by the sink; perhaps I could use it to keep his deadly beak occupied long enough for me to unpick him from his owner and get him back into his cage. The nails would have to wait. I grabbed the towel, tossed it over the bird and stood back. Somewhere underneath, Charlie wriggled, screamed, chewed and blustered furiously.

"Don't worry," I gasped with some relief, "I think we've got him now."

"He's still got my ear, though!" the landlady wailed as the towelled mass on her shoulder threw itself about.

Before picking up the entrapped parrot it would be prudent to ascertain where the beak-bearing head end was. I took a pencil and gently prodded the stuffed towel. With a crisp crack the pencil was split into two and fell apart; I had found the head end. Without losing more time I grabbed hold of the part that was probably the plump little belly and tugged hard. The parrot tugged hard at the lady's ear. Her shrieking resumed. Feeling in need of reinforcement, I took off my white surgery coat and threw that on top of the towel, completely covering the woman's head. As best I could I felt for the parrot's head, held it and set about releasing the grip on the mutilated ear. The landlady put both her hands on the hidden bird and allowed me to try to detach the claw dug into her shoulder. When I got beneath the towelling I found that the other claw was now also firmly attached to her shoulder. Charlie was no pushover.

Suddenly I realized that I was touching the very things

that had been the cause of all the bother: the overgrown nails. I carefully lifted a corner of the towel and looked at them. There they all were, side by side. A perfect opportunity! With the vicious end of Charlie still gurgling and spitting somewhere higher up in the folds of material I might well be able to do my stuff—if I had my clippers. Then I remembered that they were still lying somewhere in the décolletage of the buxom lady who stood before me, my white coat draped over her head and both hands clasped to a jumble of protesting towelling on her shoulder.

"Er, I can do his nails very well now," I began. "I've got his claws out perfectly. Can you hold on like that for a few moments more?"

"Yes, but get on with it. My ear's hurting like hell. Little beggar. Get on with it!"

"Er, well, my clippers . . . you've got my clippers in your . . ."

"I know. Get them out. I can't hold him much longer!"

"I'll have to put my hand down your dress, madam. . . ."

"Of course you will. GET ON WITH IT!"

Squeezing my fingers together rather as if I were preparing to lamb a ewe, I entered the talcumed valley and probed downwards in search of my instrument. When my unwilling hand was completely within her dress and I was beginning to worry about just how far down I was going to have to go, I mercifully felt metal lodged behind some item of twangy underwear.

"I'm awfully sorry about all this," I was saying in embarrassed confusion as I pinned the clippers between two fingers and began to extract them. Then the surgery door opened and Edith, the receptionist, came in. My hand was still down the front of the landlady's dress.

"Just cutting the parrot's toenails, Edith," I explained brightly.

Edith was a non-conformist lay preacher, and I often wondered whether she treated her Maker with the same brisk and relentless efficiency which could be a source of terror to both slow-paying farmers and ham-fisted young veterinarians. She glared icily through her spectacles and backed briskly out again. Meanwhile I had re-armed myself with the clippers and started to trim the bird's claws. Following my plan to cut back a little at a time, I pruned them bit by bit to what seemed a more reasonable length. When I had finished I noticed that the end of each nail was showing a little blood. It was only the merest drop but I had obviously cut back just a fraction too far. I dabbed each nail with a styptic liquid to seal it up neatly.

At last Charlie, almost apoplectic with rage, was securely back in his cage. The landlady adjusted her dress, I put some antiseptic on her abused ear, bandaged her wounded fingers, sponged her down and talked soothingly about what lovable if naughty little fellows these parrots were. She seemed reassured and even grateful, and if anyone's dignity had suffered wounds from our experience, it apparently was not hers.

To my dismay, Charlie's owner and his vet did not bear the only physical wounds from our encounter that morning, for Charlie had not been gone from my surgery for more than ten minutes before his toenails began to bleed again. It was only after ten days and considerable care that the intermittent bleeding completely stopped. On subsequent visits I learned to handle him more deftly, and the experience also taught me something about cutting the sensitive nails of other Charlies to come.

There were plenty of them, for Manchester parrots seemed particularly prone to overgrown toenails, to diarrhoeas that resisted treatment because the unco-operative birds steadfastly refused to take their medicines, to coughs and sneezes that resisted treatment because the unco-operative microbes causing these complaints just as steadfastly ignored my medicaments, and to baldness. The baldness was self-inflicted—the parrots persistently plucked out all their feathers (except the ones on the top of their heads, of course) until they became pink-nude, pot-bellied and scrawny-necked. They reminded me of bellicose miniature Colonel Blimps emerging from the Turkish baths. I could find no itchy skin parasites or nutritional deficiency to cause this craze for full frontal exhibitionism.

My failure to counter what seemed sheer cussedness on the part of my malevolent parrot patients was underlined by the raucous cursing that they heaped upon me week after week as I surveyed the results of my impotent efforts to grow even one single plume on their old men's bodies. What irritated me about the nudists was their sheer cheek; having extracted almost all its plumage, one of these infuriating creatures would sit on its perch, tilt a choleric, red-rimmed eye in my direction—and then shiver. Of course you'll shiver, you dum-dum! I wanted to shout in my frustration. If I had had the temerity to write a considered dissertation on the Diseases of the Parrot, it would have consisted of but two sentences, written in blood on the finest parchment: "Parrots are incontinent, wheezing asthmatics in need of chiropody and tungsten-wire whole-body toupees. They get well if they feel like it, or they don't."

Nevertheless, I had to carry on. Dump the parrots and there might never be any condors or cassowaries or King penguins. And I had to do something to reassure the doting owners that Rochdale was the Mecca for infirm and irascible parrots. Although my treatment of their pets' ailments seemed to be meeting with a singular lack of obvious success, I decided that at the very least I could thwart the parrot nudist brigade in its efforts to commit suicide by self-refrigeration. I was damned if I would let these birds have the last laugh by developing hypothermia or pneumonia or frostbite.

First I gave instructions for all such patients to be confined day and night for one or two weeks at least to rooms where the temperature never dropped below 80 degrees

Fahrenheit. Then it struck me that parrots really did appear to be old-fashioned sort of fellows; the analogy to Colonel Blimp really did stick. Where more genteel birds such as doves might get tipsy now and then when feasting on fermenting berries in the fall, parrots have the leery, rheumy eye of the hard-liquor drinker who prefers the grain to the grape all the year round. If the incontinent wheezers spurned my antibiotics and sulpha drugs, let's see how they fared on a drop of the hard stuff. As soon as I began to prescribe minute tots of rum or brandy for all my sick parrots I began to have successes. My knowledge of disease in exotic birds had not advanced very much, but a combination of the Turkish bath and hard-liquor regime for nearly all my cases resulted in more and more incontinent birds passing normal stools, the wheezers beginning to breathe more easily and some of the Kojak types even growing a soft covering of grey down and later the colourful plumage that was their rightful attire. As time went on the booze-'em-and-bake-'em therapy persuaded quite a few parrot owners that Dr. Whittle's partner had a knack with their favourite bird.

I also earned the rather more demonstrative gratitude of a lady almost as exotic as her pet. It all began when the surgery telephone rang as I was showing out yet another parrot owner who was looking forward to giving his wife the perfect excuse for taking out the brandy bottle as soon as he got home.

"Hello," said a sultry voice as I picked up the receiver. "Is that Dr. Taylor?"

"It is," I replied. "Who's this speaking?"

"It's Miss Seksi. I expect you've heard of me. I'm the speciality danseuse at the Garden of Eden."

This surprising statement did not perplex me as it might have done, for I knew of the Garden of Eden, a sleazy Manchester night-club from whose doors there wafted a permanent smell of stale beer, yesterday's cigars and cheap perfume.

"What can I do for you, Miss, er, Seksi?" I asked. Edith looked up sharply from her book-keeping.

"Well, it's very confidential. Private, if you know what I mean."

"I see, but how can I help? Do you wish me to visit or will you come to the surgery?"

"Well, if you can be sure it's all confidential I'll come with him to the surgery if you'll give me an appointment."

"Er . . . come with who, Miss, er, Miss Seksi?"

"My Oscar, of course."

Who or what was her Oscar? I doubted if she had won a Hollywood Academy Award and decided Oscar must be a friend or husband. Well, I thought, she must realize I'm not a people doctor. We had had cases of Pakistanis and displaced persons from Eastern Europe queuing patiently for hours among the dogs, cats and budgerigars in the waiting room, only to find when it was their turn that we did not extract human teeth or issue National Health Service sick notes. This lady sounded one hundred per cent English, but she still wanted me to treat this chap Oscar. Then again, I thought, I had had a few human patients. There was the window cleaner who regularly had our fiery horse linament for his arthritic knee, many a farmer swore our medicaments were the most likely to cure the ringworm he had contracted from his calves, and I had dealt with all sorts of problems from impetigo to impotence among the hill-farming folk of the Pennines, who found it easier to talk to the vet, sitting over a cup of tea in the farmhouse after calving a cow, than to the doctor in his surgery in town.

"But, er, are you and Oscar bringing the animal?" I asked Miss Seksi.

"I work with Oscar. Oscar is my python."

"Oh," I said, grateful that at any rate part of the mystery had been solved.

A confidential consultation, with no nurse and no assistant present, was arranged for the ailing Oscar for three o'clock, and I waited in intrigued anticipation. Punctually at three, a taxi pulled up outside the waiting-room door and Edith ushered in a startlingly painted lady of Junoesque proportions dressed in an imitation tiger-skin coat that seemed to be afflicted here and there with remarkably accurate imitations of sarcoptic mange. She teetered on six-inch stiletto heels, lugging awkwardly in one hand a large canvas bag. As she sat down she dabbed the perspiration from her face and touched up the paintwork expertly. Then she switched on the multi-volt smile that had been designed to cut its way through cigar smoke, wolf whistles, rude remarks and embarrassing silence with the ease of a disposable scalpel. Her first words to me were "Bloody heavy, he is, poor little darlin'."

Undoing some cord tied tightly around the neck of the canvas bag, Miss Seksi switched off the head-splitting smile and plunged an arm inside. Slowly she withdrew a glistening, plump snake, an anaconda that must have been every bit of twelve feet long.

"There he is," said my client. "Poor, poor Oscar; I'm really worried about him."

"What seems to be the problem?" I faltered, looking down the undulating length of Miss Seksi's partner as he gently wound himself round her shoulders and waist. His weight seemed normal and there was a healthy fluorescent glint as the light caught his rippling scales. Oscar was trying to disappear inside Miss Seksi's fur coat. Already the first six feet of him were making her torso bulge and warp beneath her coat as if she were made of rubber; in a moment my patient would have gone completely to ground. Remembering Charlie the parrot and the fate of my toenail clippers, I firmly resolved that I was not going in there after him. Instead I grasped twelve inches of Oscar's tail end, flexed my biceps and stood firmly with my legs apart. Oscar, like all such non-venomous constrictor snakes, was ninety per cent muscle. He continued to contract his powerful twelve-foot body as I held staunchly onto his tail and refused to be pulled inside the perfumed recesses of Miss Seksi's tiger-skin coat. The result was predictable. If I was not going to release the tail and if Oscar continued doggedly to go places, there was only one thing left that had to give way: Miss Seksi. The contracting snake pulled her right into me. "Dear God, keep Edith out of here at this moment!" I prayed, as I stood nose to nose and thigh to thigh with the lady from the Garden of Eden. Oscar wedded us like Scotch tape; as he threw a loop or two around my wrist, I wondered who was holding whom.

"The, er, the problem," said Miss Seksi from two inches away, "the problem is personal. It's his eyes." She breathed a cloud of Chanel No. 5 and onions into my face. "If you can reach my handbag, Doctor, you'll find the card; you'll see what I mean."

Still clutching my bit of Oscar with one hand, I clicked open her handbag with the other, fished vaguely about inside it and pulled out an oblong card.

"That's it," she said. "That's the card from the clinic."

I had no idea what she was talking about. "What clinic?" I asked.

"The venereal disease clinic." She lowered her voice confidentially and looked at the door to make sure it was firmly closed. "I think Oscar's got it."

"Got what, venereal disease?"

"Yes. You see, Oscar and I are in the burlesque business. We've appeared in Paris and Beirut, haven't we, Oscar?" Oscar's head had emerged from below Miss Seksi's coat and, with flicking tongue, he had begun to investigate my shoes. "Yes, we've been very well received, Oscar and I. Very exotique, very good money."

"But how do you and Oscar work together?"

"I'm a speciality danseuse . . . exotique . . . you know."

"A stripper?" I hazarded.

Miss Seksi gave me a five-second, full-power burst of the smile. "Yes, but not low-class, my dear," she said. "Seksi's my stage name; actually it's Schofield."

"Please go on, Miss Schofield."

"Well, during our act I do a very exotique speciality dance as Cleopatra. See what I mean? That's where Oscar fits in."

An embryonic glimmer of light began to spark in my brain. We bumped foreheads.

"During the act—it went down *awfully* well in Beirut—I disrobe to exotique music" (Miss Schofield emphasized the *tique* each time she uttered her favourite word) "and the climax, when I'm in the buff—you know what I mean, Doctor—is when I commit suicide."

"So Oscar is Cleopatra's asp?"

"Exactly. Oscar is the asp. Rather exotique, don't you think?"

If Cleopatra really did shuffle off this mortal coil with the aid of a reptile it must have been one of the small venomous Egyptian snakes, possibly a cobra, but certainly not a 65-pound South American constrictor.

"Yes, Doctor," went on Miss Seksi. "My agent thinks it's a really dramatic finale, with Oscar twining all round my body."

"I see, I see," I interposed quickly.

"Now. The thing is, Doctor, I've had a touch of, er, VD. The clinic gave me cards to hand out to anybody I might have had what they call contact with. I've dished out the cards, of course, though I couldn't care a fig for my boy friends—they're all pigs. But Oscar, he's my partner, my little darling. He's everything to me."

"Why do you think Oscar might have picked up an infection from you?"

"His eyes, Doctor, look at his eyes. I'm worried sick by them. It's his work, Doctor. He's got it from me, I'm sure."

Miss Seksi was becoming tearful. We were still so closely entangled that any sobbing on her part was likely to soak my tie.

"Trouble is," she continued, "the clinic wouldn't see him, even though I told them all about him, how he worked with me. That's the National Health Service for you! So that's why I came to you."

"Let's get ourselves sorted out and have a look at his head," I said. My own head was spinning. Whatever it was that did not look right with his eyes, it certainly could not be VD. That disease of humans does not affect other mammals, and in reptiles like Oscar it is out of the question. Although, I reflected, I could not be positive that no scientific paper had ever been published stating categorically that anacondas and their like were immune to the gonorrhoea microbe.

Eventually Miss Seksi/Schofield unravelled the snake and I took a relieved step backwards. For the first time I had a good view of his head. "Look at his eyes, Doctor!" his owner wailed. "They've gone like that in less than a week!"

Both the anaconda's eyes were indeed abnormal. Instead of being limpid dark jewels they were blind, milk-white blobs. Looking at them carefully through the magnifying lens of an ophthalmoscope with its intense beam of light, I was able to make out the eye lying beneath the milky film.

"When did Oscar last shed his skin?" I asked. I had not seen this eye condition in snakes before, but an idea was forming in my mind.

"About a week or ten days ago. Came off as clean as a whistle."

"And round about then you first noticed his eyes?"

"Yes."

Snakes' eyes are completely covered by a non-moving transparent third eyelid. As the rest of the skin is shed from time to time as the animal grows, the old outer layers of the third eyelid are sloughed too. Or rather they should be. I was convinced that the "VD" infection of Oscar's eyes was the old third eyelid which had not fallen off with the rest of the skin. It was a sheet of tough, dead tissue covering an otherwise healthy eye.

While I prepared to try and restore the sight of the uncomplaining trouper there and then, his owner became tearful again. "If he's blind, I won't be able to work with him any more," she moaned. I did not quite see how vision was essential for Oscar's act. "How can I replace him? I just couldn't get another like him. It would mean back to my Florence Nightingale routine—and at half the salary." The wailing increased as I dropped a little paraffin oil into each of the white eyes.

"Hold tightly onto his head, please," I instructed. Oscar began once again to intertwine us both, and I felt his rear end drag me into another bout of intimate contact with his mistress. The latter was now red-faced and sweating as well as weepy. Even her mask of make-up was beginning to erode.

With a pair of fine-toothed forceps I gently began to tease up the edge of the white film covering one of the snake's eyes. Bit by bit, and using more drops of oil as I progressed, I slowly freed the crust. A dark gold glint showed that Oscar's eye lay uninjured underneath. At last the entire piece of dead tissue came away. Oscar eyed me, unblinking and inscrutable. I set to work on the other side of the head and soon the second eye was clear as well. The "VD" had gone. Putting down my instruments, I struggled out of Oscar's coils and stood back to survey my handiwork.

Miss Seksi was open-mouthed in astonishment and delight, gurgling and smiling real, unprofessional smiles. Releasing Oscar's head and letting him roam where he would, she came over and hugged me. "Doctor, how can I ever thank you?" she purred. Then she imprisoned me in a python-like embrace and planted a big, soggy, bright red kiss on my forehead, just as Edith came back into the surgery.

"Ah, you're just in time, Edith . . . " I said.

"So I see," she interrupted drily.

" . . . to help get Oscar back into his bag."

Between us we untangled the now clear-eyed anaconda, and Edith saw Miss Seksi out.

"We can do without that sort," she said, coming back into the room where I was sterilizing the forceps.

For all her stagey manner, Miss Seksi had enlivened my afternoon, and there was nothing artificial or overblown about Oscar: he had provided my first experience of what I later found to be a common problem in snakes.

"Oh no, we can't, Edith," I replied.

5
Belle. Vue

Although it was now almost two years since I had joined
Norman Whittle in his practice, I seemed to be no nearer the
solid diet of zoo cases that I craved. Without a background
of zoo-animal experience I was frequently forced into tight
corners where my ignorance was nakedly exposed. It was not
just the difficulty of diagnosing a whole new range of diseases
in animals that figured nowhere in orthodox veterinary
education—there were times when I could not even put a
name to the species of creature that was borne, dragged or
prodded into the consulting room. Animal owners often do
not take kindly to the veterinarian working with pet cats
and dogs who has forgotten the name of "Fluffy", "Poochie",
"Garibaldi" or whatever in the time between visits, even
though these may be years apart. The position was consider-
ably trickier when a furry brown creature about as big as a
ferret and with large orange eyes with pinpoint pupils was
proudly plonked down on the table and the owner said,
"Horace, this is Dr. Taylor. Be a good boy now," and then
continued, "I've brought Horace down from Carlisle, Doctor, because the zoo told me your practice could get rid of
this skin disease that's been bothering him for months."

Having travelled 110 miles with this whatever-it-was, the
smiling owner of Horace would not be impressed if I started
off by asking what sort of beast I was dealing with. He was
absolutely certain I knew. I looked at the Horace and the

63

Horace gazed gently back to me. He seemed docile enough as he moved slowly around the table top. Anyway, he had to be a mammal because he was hairy.

"He's got these small bald patches on his head, Doctor," the proud owner announced.

I looked at the Horace's head; it was mongoose-like, with small ears and a pretty damp nose about the size of a chihuahua's.

"Well, well," I began hopefully, "it's not often we see one of these." The idea of this artful gambit was to lead the owner into giving me the clue I needed by agreeing that crunchlappets or flummerjacks or whatever the thing was were indeed getting rarer.

The owner of Horace did not fall into my rhetorical snare. "No, Doctor," he replied, "but Mr. So-and-so says that Dr. Whittle's practice did wonders with his when it was sick." Impasse.

I looked at Horace's feet; they were finger-like and reminded me of a monkey's. Although there was not much sign of anything to grab hold of I decided to stall for time by first stroking Horace and then picking him up so that I could get a better look at the diseased areas. He diffidently sniffed my fingers as I approached him. To my horror, as I stroked him I felt his backbone. Horace had a backbone like all mammals, but what chilled me as I ruffled through his fur was that the spines of his vertebrae appeared actually to be jutting out through his skin; my fingers were pressing directly on his spinal column! He seemed plump enough and there had been no talk of an accident—why on earth should Horace's owner be worrying about bald patches when there was something much more dramatically significant happening to his beloved pet's back? Perhaps I could get through the examination, diagnosis and treatment without actually knowing what Horace was. No, that was a hopeless idea. I was a fool—I should have admitted my ignorance as soon as Horace arrived.

At this juncture Horace decided to bite me. He did it once, precisely and powerfully, on the index finger which I was using to feel his spine. He then gazed gently at me once more as I jerked back my hand with a yelp and stuck the bleeding digit in my mouth.

"Oh my, Horace," exclaimed his owner, "that's a naughty boy. Still, I suppose you get lots of those in your job, Doctor, dealing with the likes of him."

My finger was bleeding copiously and hurt like hell, but

at least Horace had given me the chance I needed to save my ridiculous dignity. "I'll just nip and get a Band-aid," I said and slipped smartly out of the consulting room.

In thirty seconds I had plastered up the punctured finger and shot upstairs to my collection of zoo books. Somewhere in there, God willing, I would track down the Horace animal. Feverishly I flicked through the pages of an encyclopaedia of the animal kingdom. Horace's fingers seemed to be the crucial feature, but then I remembered his strange protruding spine. Not a monkey and yet not really like one of the small carnivores such as a stoat. There was nothing like him in the mongoose line. I turned to the raccoon family—maybe Horace was a cacomistle, whatever that looked like. I found the photograph of the cacomistle. Yes, the face was similar but the ears were too big and the clawed feet were most un-finger-like.

Hoping I would remember the appearance of a cacomistle should one ever be brought to me, I hurried hopefully on to the chapter dealing with the pro-simians, that strange bunch of individuals who lie halfway between insect-eating carnivores and monkeys. Horace certainly had some of the typical appearance of an insectivore, as well as those monkey-like fingers. Bingo! As I looked at the appealing faces of these most distant cousins of Man, the aye-aye, the tree-shrew and the rest, I suddenly found myself faced by an illustration of Horace in glorious colour. "Long time since I was bitten by a potto," I said gaily as I opened the door of the consulting room.

Pottos, the caption to Horace's picture stated, have horny processes on their spinal columns that project through their skin, so at least my fears about what had appeared to be Horace's exposed backbone were set at rest. He was my first pro-simian patient, though, and of pro-simian ailments I knew not a thing, but by taking scrapings and swabs of his bald patches for analysis I would try to find out what was causing the hair loss.

About a week later, Edith handed me the laboratory report on the scrapings I had taken. It started, "Your sample from a ?dotto??? (what breed of cat is that—or is it a joke?) . . ."

I would have to become accustomed to folk thinking that I was some sort of nut addicted to practical jokes. I would learn to wait patiently while the person answering the phone at a pharmaceutical company scoffed disbelievingly when a vet from Rochdale ordered some special tropical drug for bilharzia in baboons, or when the international cable operators stopped me in mid-dictation of some urgent message containing phrases like "Suggest your penguins have got bumblefoot" with a "Come off it, mate, is this an April-fool thing or something?" Years later I had to threaten an operator with legal action if he did not type out my cable about a deadly serious matter which concerned not a potto, nor indeed any kind of wild animal, but a footballer. The star player of the famous Real Madrid soccer team in Spain had contracted a unique fungus infection of his knee bone; he might well never play again. The fungus infection had never previously been recorded in humans, but the Spanish doctors knew that I had been involved in treating various kinds of fungus infection in zoo animals. They contacted me via my friends, the directors of Madrid Zoo, and I cabled what information I had concerning the fungus. I suppose one can excuse the disbelief of the cable operator as I began to dictate: "Concerning the footballer's kneecap, I know of one case of an otter in Africa and one possible hedgehog . . . ." Eventually the cable was accepted, and I like to think that the otter and the hedgehog helped that soccer star to play again.

The rest of the lab report on Horace the potto read: " . . . is positive for Trichophyton sp.—Ringworm." I handed the report back to Edith and sighed as I wrote a prescription for Horace's owner to pick up that would in time completely clear his pet's ringworm. Even if a potto was unusual, his skin disease was anything but. Would I never be let into the zoo?

67

After two and a half years of treating cats and dogs, pigs and cows, with the occasional potto or python to bring me tantalizingly close to zoo work, I was all ears when Norman Whittle casually broke some news one winter's day as we both stood warming the seats of our pants in front of the gas fire in our little office. "There's a new director been appointed at Belle Vue. Name of Legge. Got a first-class reputation as a naturalist and particularly with fish."

Could this at last be the opportunity for me to begin doing some of the real zoo veterinary work? A new director could well mean a brand new approach to the management of the animals. The zoo had recently been taken over by an international hotel and leisure group, there were rumours of new animal houses to be built and new species to be exhibited. It sounded like the perfect chance for a young, green veterinarian to get in at the beginning of a fresh chapter. I tackled Norman about it at once.

"You know how I feel about exotic animals," I said, "but I don't seem to be getting anywhere with the odds and ends, the parrots, bush babies and monkeys, that come here from time to time. I learned more when I went with you as a student to Belle Vue."

Norman knew what I was going to ask him. "Zoo work," he said, screwing up his face pensively and rocking back and forth on his heels. "Do you think there's a future in it?"

"I'm absolutely certain there is."

"As I've told you before, we don't know much about what we're doing down there, David. Can't handle most of the animals. Guesswork, inspired guesswork, most of it. It's the know-how of keepers like Matt Kelly that counts. They call us in as a formality."

"But it's one of the biggest zoos in Britain; there must be a vast amount of work for us. What about nutrition, preventive medicine, fertility improvement? There must be limitless scope for things that only a vet can do. And with a keen new director. . ."

"You may be right, but I don't go very often, you know. In the past they've called me only when they've got themselves into a sticky hole. We're the last resort."

"But if they don't appreciate veterinary work in the zoo, we should get involved deeper, show them, force them to see the value. The new company and new director mean a chance for new attitudes."

Norman sighed and slowly shook his head. "We don't know enough about these creatures. We haven't the tools. You know how it is; if a gorilla gets a bad eye they ask some specialist in humans from the eye infirmary to look at it. He comes along if and when he can spare the time, but he's used to humans who don't break both your arms and chew the top off of your ophthalmoscope if you try shining bright lights in their sore eyes. So the specialist loses interest and the case isn't followed through. A bunch of human surgeons from the university come to take blood from the lions, and three lions die because the anaesthetist doesn't have a clue what frightening things morphine does to cats. So they try again, this time using a barbiturate, and another one never wakes up. It's rather depressing. You'd find it very hard to break into that sort of set-up."

The story of the dead lions I had heard before. It made me angry then and the thought of it still does.

"Doctors be damned," I said. "It's the veterinary surgeon who should be in charge of the health of every one of those animals in Belle Vue."

My partner laughed but there was sadness in his eyes. "You're right, but you'll have a rugged time trying to convince some folk. Most of the time, with things like rhino and giraffe, I'm completely in the dark. The best I can do is to treat zebras like horses, giraffes and camels like cattle, lions and tigers like domestic cats."

"But that leaves out most of the animal kingdom. What about reptiles, primates, things like tapirs and elephants and porcupines?"

Norman shrugged. "Hobson's choice. Follow first principles."

"And animals die."

"Yes. And I have to admit that even at post-mortem I can't usually be sure why a creature gave up the ghost. Now and again I can do something positive, but mostly it's terribly frustrating. Anyway, remember we are a mixed farm and small-animal practice—don't you think the zoo could well be more trouble than it's worth?"

Norman's last sentence chilled me. I did not care to hear him even hinting that we might consider pulling out of zoo work. It was my only chance of penetrating the world of wildlife medicine. He—we—must not lose heart. Fearfully I asked, "Would you seriously think of dropping the zoo?"

"Well, it's twelve miles away, the city traffic's getting worse, all the rest of our work is round Rochdale, there are practices nearer to the zoo than us."

I felt my pulse quicken. If Norman went on in this vein his next words would surely be the renunciation of the one thing that I felt made our partnership special: the collection of strange and wonderful beasts in Belle Vue that fascinated me so powerfully. The very possibility made me shiver. I made up my mind immediately: nailing my colours to the mast with brass studs that hold firm to this day, I said, "Let me take over the work at Belle Vue. I want to make something of exotic medicine."

Norman smiled again and slipped on his white coat. It was time for surgery. "OK," he said, "that's fine by me."

At last I was going to do the zoo work; now all I needed was for the zoo to ring and report a sick animal. I made sure the other members of the staff understood that it would not matter whether I was on or off duty, I must be informed immediately the new zoo director called. God forbid that it should happen when I was in the middle of a difficult calving out on the moors!

A week went by. My visiting list consisted solely of dogs, cats, cows and pigs. Another week came, and another, and still whenever the telephone jangled it was the same sort of request: "Got a heifer here with a bloated stomach that's tight as a drum," or "Our old bitch is drinking day and night and gone off her legs." Just when I was beginning to wonder whether the Belle Vue stock had been given a bunch of remarkably effective amulets as well as a new director, the message I had been waiting for came in. A young camel that was being raised on the bottle was having problems with its mouth. Could the vet please attend?

I was delighted as I set off for Manchester. Here was an animal made for my opening performance: easy to handle and with few anaesthetic problems. I reckoned I knew a thing or two about mouths. Camels' teeth resemble cattle's, and I had pulled out dozens of those. Tongue infections, ulcers, oral forms of cancer, foreign bodies: I had no qualms about dental work and I had covered, so I thought, the whole field in pet and farm animals as well as the odd new-world monkey with so-called South American primate disease, which deforms the facial bones and scatters the growing tooth buds in bizarre disarray. I hoped camels were not prone to some esoteric mouth complaint afflicting them and them alone, murrain of the Pyramids or Gobi Desert tooth rot or some such pestilence, about which I had not read but which was common knowledge among Egyptian camel drivers and head keepers like Matt Kelly.

The road from Rochdale to the zoo in Manchester ran past an unbroken succession of terraced houses with sooty brick facades, cluttered corner shops that sold everything from a yard of elastic to sweet Cyprus sherry from the barrel, and towering mills with massive iron and brass mill gates and names like Bee and King emblazoned in white on the sweating red brick of their chimneys. It was an easy, familiar journey for me. As a small boy and later as a student I had often taken the yellow and orange double-decker bus that ran to the city and then rattled out by tram to the zoo, which stood behind high walls in a wilderness of mean streets, coal mines and railway sidings. This was the unloveliest part of the city, where sparrows sported uniformly sooty black plumage, where the vagrant and ubiquitous pigeons limped along dripping gutters with swollen, arthritic joints and gouty feet, and where the sulphurous fogs of autumn condensed on the clouded-glass windows of the tap rooms of the Engineers Arms and the Lancashire Fusiliers. Today the mills, the dreary dwellings and the churches standing shuttered and forgotten in yards of weeds and broken glass went by unnoticed. I was going to the zoo as its official vet.

Within the high walls of Belle Vue the jungle began. In the grey desert of Manchester there existed this oasis where wild creatures from every part of the globe were to be found. Just beyond the box office on the busy main road, a stone's throw from the mighty pit-shaft wheel of the Bradford colliery and within spitting distance of the London Midland and Scottish railway yard, were Africa and Asia, the impenetrable green of the Mato Grosso and the endless horizon of the steppes. There was no more than an acre of meagre, consumptive-looking grass in the whole park, and that was planted on a bare one-inch layer of soil overlying ashes. In spring the air reeked of engine smoke and in November it stung the eyes. Yet here lurked leopard and lion, eland and elephant. Here as a boy I had scaled the walls, despite the broken glass on top, to gaze down gratis on the tigon, that curious and long-lived hybrid donated a quarter of a century ago by some maharajah, and to make faces at the bears until pursued by irate keepers. It was a magic place for me, and it seemed unbelievable that at long last I was going "on safari" professionally (at the princely fee of eight shillings and six-pence per visit) among the enchanted beasts behind the high walls.

The zoo was built when the reign of Queen Victoria was

at its zenith, when Britain ruled the waves and the flower of the Indian Empire was still in full bloom. It was thought appropriate to design the buildings in the style of Mogul India which the England of the Raj had found so much to its taste, so the animal houses were built with windows, roofs and doorways in which the sensuous curves of Islamic art were wedded firmly to the heavy, worthy Victorian ways of working wood and iron. To the crowds who came from the cotton towns by train on a line that ran right into the zoo grounds, the sea-lion house in its heyday must have seemed like a delicate pavilion transported from the palace lawns of Mysore, the sort of place where, but for the drizzle and the smog and the clank of trams from the road, one might take tiffin among the jacaranda blossom with the Colonel's lady. Gardens and long rose walks were laid out between the animal houses, artificial lakes were dug, trees and bushes were planted, and among the bushes nestled the onion domes and minarets of ornamental mosques and palaces done in stucco.

In these pleasant surroundings the Victorians could promenade and admire the wild animals held behind massive bars or beyond deep pits. When they tired of the animals they could listen to brass bands in one of the several concert halls, eat in cafés, drink in pubs or amuse themselves on carousels and coconut shies in a fairground—all within the same high-walled park. The park had its own brewery and bakery inside the grounds and the facilities for great banquets, balls and fireworks displays. As I drove through the grounds on my way to see the sick baby camel, the light growing dim with the approach of evening, I could imagine what Belle Vue had been like a century before. Even today the crumbling remains of the ornamental mosques peep out of rhododendron bushes, defying the damp and the attrition of small boys' feet who clamber over the "Keep Off" notices to reach the muezzin's turret. Despite dry rot, peeling pale blue paint, a hundred years of sea lions' splashing and the dank smell of herring impregnating the wooden Mogul arches, the pavilion still stands and there is a tiny bit of one of the rose walks, too. The thick bars are gone, new animal houses have been built of concrete and fine steel, the railway stops far short of the park now and the brewery is derelict, but here and there among the modern things like the speedway and the children's playground, an arch, a dome, a pierced screen or a fragment of curled iron winks out, conjuring up a lost age of stylish self-assurance.

The young camel to which I had been called turned out to be a friendly two-humped (Bactrian) female. As I arrived Mr. Legge and Matt Kelly were feeding her from a bottle. I introduced myself to the new director while Kelly stood silently by, frowning in surprise at my appearance. Ray Legge was a slim, pale, military-looking man in his mid-forties, with dark hair and moustache, an aquiline nose and a warm and generous smile. He was neatly dressed and moved easily, with the precision of the rock climber that he was. When he spoke, it was in the crisp, public-school accents of the army officer that he had been. Quite a dramatic change from his predecessors in the post.

He pumped my hand energetically, threatening to pulverize my knuckles. "Jolly pleased to meet you. As you know, I was at Chester Zoo but I've concentrated on aquaria over the past few years, especially Blackpool Tower aquarium. I'm a fish man really, but my mammals and birds will be brought up to scratch in the next few months. Now, let's show you this camel."

Kelly the head keeper held the animal with an expression of weary scepticism at this young vet who was all book-learning and had no idea of zoo animal management. As I inquired what seemed to be the trouble, he quietly gritted his teeth and did an impersonation of St. Ignatius Loyola staring heavenwards in a baroque painting. He had a ruddy, puckish yet handsome face and a close-cropped head that appeared dice-shaped, cubic with slightly rounded corners, the whole set on a short, stocky body. Matt had put the fear of God into me when I was a student with his apparent omniscience, a sleeveful of zoological tricks and the autocratic bearing of a sergeant-major. Now his powerful hands held open the camel's jaws.

"She isn't suckling strongly," said Legge, "and there's this white coating developed in the mouth."

I looked inside. Sure enough, the entire internal surface of the mouth was covered with a milky white membrane. "That's thrush infection," I pronounced immediately, "the fungus you see so often in human babies. You have been sterilizing your feeding bottles properly, haven't you?"

Matt Kelly cleared his throat, went redder, but said nothing.

"Yes, Matt boils the bottles before each feed," replied the director. "Can it be serious?"

"No, not usually. We'll soon have that right. Hold on a minute."

I went to my car and brought back a bottle of gentian violet solution. While Matt held the camel's mouth open again, I used a small brush to paint the bitter purple liquid over her gums, teeth and lips. The animal screwed up her face at the taste and bubbled out a foam of purple saliva, staining Matt's hands. Gentian violet does not wash off easily. Matt's face was now plum-coloured and I feared his teeth-gritting might shatter every tooth in his head.

"Right," I said, "that'll do the trick." Confidently I said my farewells and set off home with the conviction that I had made the best possible start.

Two days later the zoo telephoned again. It was Matt Kelly. "This here camel, Dr. Taylor," he said in his light Dublin brogue, "oi don't think your purple paint's done one bit of good. She's worse." And then, as if he had already decided the patient was in such a critical state that anything more I might do could not make things any worse, he added, "Ye can come down if ye like." Damn, I thought, he talks as if I'm invited to pay my last respects.

The camel was indeed worse. The white membrane was still coating much of her mouth and the animal's general condition and vitality were deteriorating alarmingly. More of the white fungus was coating the bowels and the vagina. I had never seen thrush, a usually mild, yeasty fungus, on the rampage like this, but my training at university had paid scant attention to the germ. It was regarded as an opportunist, secondary bug of little menace under normal circumstances. Yet this camel was very definitely ill. Could the thrush alone be doing that? Much later I would learn that thrush can be rather a tough and sometimes fatal infection for birds and dolphins, but at the time I felt sure the camel case was more complicated than I had first suspected.

Matt raised his eyebrows when I began to mutter my doubts about the case. "Sure, oi thought all along she wouldn't make it," he said. "Bottle-reared animals haven't the resistance." He adopted an expression of tired patience.

Suddenly something came back to me. Fungi. Yeast fungi. Yeasts, the kind of things that are used in making bread and beer. The yeasts thrive in the bread dough and, during the brewing, on sugar. Sugar, that was it. Somewhere I had read that people with excess sugar in their urine, in other words diabetics, are more susceptible to yeast fungus infections.

"I'm going to take a urine sample, Mr. Kelly," I announced. Matt stared. He had never heard of such a thing being done to a camel. Still, I could imagine him ruminating, young vets do strange things like that when they don't know where the devil they are.

With much difficulty I passed a catheter into the camel's bladder, drew off a few teaspoons of urine and dipped one of my glucose test strips into the sample. It turned deep blue—the camel was diabetic. "Sugar diabetes, Mr. Kelly," I proclaimed excitedly. Matt scowled. "Now I want some blood."

The blood test's abnormally high sugar level confirmed beyond doubt the cause of the camel's disease. The thrush was secondary and could probably be eradicated by anti-fungal drugs, but the question of how to handle the diabetes was a tricky one. I talked it over with Ray Legge.

"It looks as if she'll need a daily injection of insulin," I warned. "We'll start off with the fairly long-acting protamine zinc kind and fiddle about with the dose until she's just free of sugar."

It was not a very encouraging prospect, possibly having to give shots to a camel for life. I knew a number of dog owners who were used to jabbing their diabetic pets each day with insulin; the animals tended to develop small knobbles all over them and felt like pineapples.

"Couldn't we give anti-diabetic drugs in her food?" asked Ray.

There were at least two kinds of oral drug which were proving effective in some human cases at that time, but they had failed to reduce the sugar level and control the progress of the disease in almost all animal cases. I explained this to the zoo director and we decided to embark on the course of insulin shots. Matt Kelly was armed with a bunch of syringes and needles, and I showed him how to adjust the dose according to the colour of the test strip after it had been in contact with the urine.

"And where do oi get the urine from?" Matt inquired. "Oi can't stand waitin' behind the craytchure all day long hopin' it'll pee!"

"Of course not," I replied. "All you need do is spot a damp patch on the concrete where she's passed water and dab your test strip in that."

Matt looked at his collection of medical paraphernalia with the enthusiasm of a bilious leprechaun. Crawling about over the floor blotting up camel-juice indeed! Just what he had known would happen if novices like young Taylor started interfering.

The young camel began to put on weight and condition over the next few days as Matt gave the insulin and the anti-fungal treatment annihilated the layers of yeast fungus. Things were progressing admirably. Then, on the ninth day, the youngster refused to feed and took on a drawn and depressed look. The sugar content in the urine rocketed upwards. When Ray Legge went into the hospital on the morning of the tenth day he found the little camel lying dead. Miserable, I drove over to perform the necropsy. The pancreas, the organ which produces natural insulin normally and also serves a number of other vital functions concerning digestion of food, I found to be a shrivelled, almost non-existent piece of tissue. What there was of it was inflamed, red and yellow. Matt Kelly silently returned to me the unused syringes, test strips and injections. So much for veterinary science.

Despite this early setback, Ray Legge set off to a cracking start at Belle Vue. He supervised the building of one of the finest aquaria and reptile houses in the country and then designed a modern great ape complex complete with isolation rooms, a self-contained kitchen and food store for Len, the senior ape keeper, and underground tunnels leading from centrally heated, glass-fronted indoor quarters to circular open-air play pits again protected from the germ-bearing visitors by armour-plated glass. In these new buildings I was going to spend much of my time in the next few years, for it became a mutual, unspoken arrangement that I would visit the zoo regularly at least once a week and not just when I was called. Exciting new inhabitants for both completed residences had been purchased by the zoo, giant tortoises and alligators for the one and a pair of young gorillas for the other. These would join the existing reptiles and apes from the old reptile and great ape houses.

Ray was a stimulating and sympathetic person to work with: a talented artist and sculptor in wood and stone, he had a sensitive and humane approach to zoo animals wonderfully combined with the never-ending curiosity of the born naturalist. To hear him talk, his time with the British Army in India during the war had been one glorious natural history ramble, finding new fish, rare insects or strange plants wherever he was posted. During the Cyprus crisis, when he instructed troops hunting Eoka terrorists in the arts of mountain climbing, he found the greatest excitement in pursuing the nimble lizards of the Troodos Mountains under the concealed rifles of General Grivas's guerrilla snipers.

But it was with Matt Kelly that I had to build some sort of bridge if I was to carry out my resolve to learn something of his zoocraft. This most renowned of British head keepers had worked for many years at Belle Vue and before that at Dublin, which at the time had an unrivalled reputation for the quality of its lions. Matt was no naturalist, no lizard chaser, no smooth utterer of Latin names, no scientist; he was simply the perfect head keeper of his time. An out-and-out practical zooman, he was born with that "feel" for his animals which is to be found in good shepherds and in farmers who rear plump beef cattle efficiently and with apparent ease, not by any high-falutin knowledge of food analyses, digestibility factors or other scientist's jargon, but by observation, experience, personal attention to individual feeding and plain, inborn talent. Also, in the same indefinable way that natural seamen sense impending changes in the weather, Matt had a nose for trouble. Long before it was obvious to others, he would start to fret about the rhinoceros or the ostrich or any other of the numerous creatures that he knew so intimately.

"Matt," I said one day, shortly after the death of the baby camel, "you know I learned a lot at Belle Vue as a student. Now, doing the veterinary work myself, I'm going to need your help in showing me a whole lot more of the things a vet doesn't know."

Matt seemed pleased with my approach. A wide grin, showing broad white teeth like a chimp's, split his face. "Sure and we'll see what we can make of ye, Dr. Taylor," he replied.

Things, little things, immediately began to go wrong. If there was a wrong way to do something, some particularly obtuse, disastrous or all-fingers-and-thumbs way to do it, I did it. There was the cardinal sin of zoo keeping which I quickly committed—leaving a gate unlocked. Matt and I had been looking at the Barbary sheep as they sprang from rock to rock round the artificial mountain in their pen. Bald, scurfy areas on their coat suggested mange. I would arrange to have them trapped, take skin scrapings for examination and dip them like farm flocks. Ping, ping, ping. Surefootedly on their tiny hooves they leaped from one minute ledge to another with infinite grace. Then, just as surefootedly, one of them went ping, ping, ping out through the gate into the zoo grounds. The last in, I had not bolted the gate behind me. Red-faced, I chased after a fuming Matt Kelly as we pursued the agile creature like two decrepit satyrs on the trail of a wood nymph. Out of the zoo grounds we went and onto the main road that leads to the city centre. The Barbary sheep was gaining ground; the way it was galloping along one might have thought it was making for the docks and hoping to dash aboard a freighter due any moment to sail for its native North Africa. Eventually, with the aid of Ray Legge, keepers and sundry other citizens who had been informed of or had actually witnessed our puffing, cursing dash towards the town, the creature was cornered in a coal merchant's yard. Master of rocky pinnacles and sandstone cliff faces, the Barbary sheep found that the scree-sloped black pyramids of coal did not provide firm footing. Scrabbling vainly to reach the sooty peak of one mound it slipped relentlessly backwards and was caught.

Covered in coal dust that stuck firmly to our clothes and sweating skin, Matt and I returned to the zoo. "Jeez, ye made me purple a few weeks ago, Doctor," he lamented, clicking his teeth, "and now ye've made me black!"

Our next joint foray concerned a monkey that had been fed the most potentially deadly titbits. Every zoo attracts a tiny proportion of nuts, dangerous eccentrics and vandals among the crowds of paying public. I can understand the impulses that make folk ignore the "No Feeding" signs and pass potato chips or boiled sweets to elephants or monkeys; I detest it, but see the motivation involved, when drunken louts climb over the walls on a Saturday night after the pubs close and, in the fuddled spirit of bravado which this most primitive of mammalian species exhibits at such times, knock hell out of defenceless creatures like penguins or wallabies or peacocks. But I do not understand, cannot in my wildest dreams explain, the workings of the mind of the human who passed a bunch of thin, new, stainless-steel razor blades through the bars to a monkey. The monkey liked the look of the shining metal wafers and, so that his fellows could not purloin them, put them safely away—in his mouth. Like anyone who has received a present of which he is rather proud, the monkey just had to keep taking them out from time to time to admire and shuffle through them, and it was while he was inspecting his treasure in this way that his keeper spotted the blades and raised the alarm. Quick as a flash, the monkey put his fascinating little collection back into his cheek pouch.

When Matt and I arrived the monkey stared innocently at us. No blood ran from his mouth. His fingers appeared uninjured. Razor blades? What razor blades? his eyes seemed to say. Like some Indian fakir, he had so far avoided doing himself harm by manipulating the blades delicately with his soft tongue and velvety cheek lining. But how were we to retrieve them? I still had no speedy, safe monkey anaesthetics. If we netted him, might he not slice up the inside of his mouth in the fracas?

"What do you think, Matt?" I asked my mentor. "How do we get the bloody things out without carving him up?"

Matt thought for a moment; then, with an air of relaxed confidence, he said, "Get me a sweepin' brush."

I found a brush for Matt, who slipped into the cage through the trapdoor at the back. The monkey darted to a far corner well away from him and prepared to do battle. It was obvious the head keeper was going to try to pin him in the corner with the brush. OK, the monkey was clearly thinking, we would see about that, and he tensed his powerful leg muscles, ready to leap out of the way of the imminent onslaught. With all the space available, the monkey must have reckoned that by jumping rapidly round from bars to branch to ledge to bars again he could wear out this lumbering human with his unwieldy brush in a war of attrition that might, as far as he was concerned, last all day. My forecast of the outcome, inexperienced as I was, agreed with that of my little simian friend; if I had been a betting man, I would have laid my money on the monkey.

Both of us were barking up the wrong tree. Matt's battle plan was quite, quite different. Without warning the stocky Irishman began to shout and swear at the top of his voice. Every oath invented in the isle of saints and sinners came blasting out. His face contorted with rage and he waved the brush vigorously about, clouting it with resounding bangs on the walls of the cage. It was an unholy din, but he did not make one move towards the monkey, nor did he bring his weapon within feet of the startled animal's crouching body. To the monkey it must have seemed as though the head keeper had gone mad. Any second this Fury would bring the flailing brush smashing down on his puny frame. With wrath like this he would not be just pinned and caught, he would be smashed to smithereens! This was going to be no game, but a matter of life or death somehow to keep out of range of the murderous maniac. He was going to have to run and run and run.

When running for your life you discard all inessential baggage so, watching for the first thunderbolt, the monkey

picked the razor blades out of his mouth and dropped them on the floor. Matt stopped shouting, put down his brush, replaced the expression of mock rage with one of twinkling satisfaction and gathered up the slivers of steel. "That's the way ye do it, Dr. Taylor," he said. "Now we can bag him and ye can check him over if ye like."

I was very impressed. Catching the monkey in a sort of butterfly net did not take long, then the captive was transferred without ceremony to a sack for carrying across to the hospital. When we arrived there the bagful of monkey was put on the table and I prepared to do my bit. I would sedate the monkey with a small shot of barbiturate so that I could examine him. I had the choice of injecting through the sack—an unhygienic procedure—or fishing the animal out, putting a full nelson on him and doing it elegantly in arm or thigh. I decided to extract him, but which end of him was where? There were three or four moving lumps in the wriggling sack, but were they arms, head or buttocks? I reckoned that one spherical lump must be the head and seized it firmly through the sacking. It was not the head— it was the other end. A second later the dagger-like fang teeth of the genuine head end lanced through the sack and sliced my left index finger almost in half. As I tried to stem the bleeding and prepared to go down to the city hospital for suturing and tetanus injections, Matt gave me the word. "Never try grabbin' a monkey in a bag like that again, Doctor. Remember his eyes are pressed close to the coarse sackin' stuff. Ye can't see where he is, but sure as hell he can see ye."

Painfully I acknowledged my dumb stupidity and went off to the Manchester hospital, where the house surgeon declined to use one drop of local anaesthetic as he cobbled together my sliced extremity. (My colleagues in human surgery do not realize how easy their primate species are to handle; try doing the same on a young chimp, for example.) He also cauterized the wound deeply and painfully with silver nitrate, neglected to give me any antibiotics and consequently produced a throbbing infection.

It was when the finger was at last settling down and my hand was once more available to do surgery on my own behalf that Ray Legge informed me that one of the zoo's golden pheasants had a lump on its eyelid. When I examined the bird there was no doubt that the hard, yellowish swelling was a tumour, but not very difficult to cut out. I decided to take the bird back to my surgery in Rochdale and do the small operation under gas anaesthesia. Matt Kelly came along with me.

With its striking art-nouveau plumage of scarlet, green, gold and black, the golden pheasant is one of the handsomest birds in the world and definitely among my favourites. Like many other species of pheasant, the male sports a particularly gorgeous flourish of tail feathers, and it was on one such exquisite avian dandy that I was operating. All went well as I cut out the growth with scalpel and forceps and Edith puffed air and a minute quantity of halothane gas into the syrup tin containing the head of the slumbering bird. Matt watched and seemed moderately impressed. After stitching the wound with fine nylon thread, I told Edith to stop the anaesthetic and stood back to admire my work. The bird drowsed peacefully on the operating table. Then, as is the way with birds coming out of anaesthesia, it suddenly blinked its eyes open, flipped itself up onto its feet and fluttered off the table before any of us could move. Rapidly gaining strength, and finding itself in surroundings quite different from its native Tibetan forests or its range at Belle Vue, it dashed merrily round the room, knocking over light pieces of equipment and provoking the cats who sat in wire-mesh boxes waiting their turn for surgical attention. Edith and I gathered our wits and set about retrieving the energetic post-op patient.

"Careful!" shouted Kelly, crouching down in the posture of a rugby full-back about to tackle his man. "Leave him to me! I'll get him as he comes round!"

But we took no notice and scuttled in hot pursuit, while Matt waited to bag the pheasant as it dashed towards him on its next lap of the room. Anxious to impress the head keeper with my animal handling expertise, I ungallantly elbowed Edith out of the way, put on a spurt and made a determined grab.

"Leave him to me!" Matt yelled again, but I had caught the bird—or so I thought. With a firm grasp of the careering pheasant's proud tail feathers, I applied the brakes and the long plumes came to a halt. The pheasant, to my horror, dashed on, straight into Matt's arms. Now bereft of its full complement of the tiger-barred plumes which in the complete bird make up an arching tail of just the right artistic length, the pheasant was exposing a stubby, yellow-pink butt end reminiscent of a Christmas turkey on Boxing Day.

"Dammit, look!" groaned Matt, his teeth grinding as he struggled to contain more picturesque Irish turns of phrase while Edith was present. "Look at the bird's ar . . . posterior!"

Although unhurt, the bird looked most undignified as it squatted in Matt's folded arms. Both of them, I thought, looked at me with a red and reproachful eye. There was no way of making up for my mistake, no glue nor subterfuge could save my face. It would be many months before nature restored the pheasant's fine cockade and covered the evidence of my ineptitude.

Matt's sour expression confirmed that I had done it again. "Never catch hold of a bird loike that again," he instructed as he made for the door and I stood glumly, still clutching my wretched bunch of feathers like a schoolboy caught in the act of picking the neighbour's strawberries. "And give me those feathers," he added, holding out a hand. "Dozens of schoolchildren ask me for such things." I could imagine him handing this lot out and saying in his fruity brogue, "And these were pulled out of a golden pheasant by a clumsy young vet. Can ye imagine that?" I was not building much yet in the way of bridges with Mr. Matt Kelly, that was certain.

At least Ray Legge was encouraging and tolerant as I stumbled my way painfully through the minefield of practice among creatures too dangerous or too difficult to handle safely, who presented symptoms that bore no resemblance to anything I had seen in cat or pig or carthorse. I also had to contend with techniques of animal self-defence which I had not met before, from the torpid sloth who is anything but slothful when slashing rapidly and accurately with its front claws, to the coatimundi who, if you pick it up by its tail and hold it safely at arm's length, will athletically climb up its own tail and summarily deal with you. It shares this contortionist ability with the opossum, Matt instructed me. It came as a relief sometimes, though one which I would have vehemently denied at the time, to return at the end of a day of "guess-agnosis" at the zoo and get stuck into a surgery full of common or garden domestic pets with complaints that seemed like old and trusted friends, where drugs acted predictably and surgery was a romp round anatomy as familiar as one's own back yard.

Matt Kelly continued to supervise my enthusiastic meddling with a melancholy reserve. My wrong diagnoses were shown up when I performed post-mortems. The square-faced Irishman would click his teeth as I prodded around inside the cadaver of an antelope that I had considered to be afflicted with liver infection but whose diseased lungs were manifestly the cause of its death. "Knew it hadn't much chance," he would opine as I began to mutter the Latin name of the condition and hopelessly try to baffle him with science. "Seen it before, oi have, Dr. Whittle and oi both. Knew the powders ye gave him would do no good." Matt would shake his head and reflect aloud on the good old days when yoghurt, cider vinegar, honey and molasses had been the elixirs of life in the zoo and everything from axolotl to zebra had apparently expired only from advanced old age.

It seemed that the only common fact about exotic species was their unwillingness to exhibit symptoms that had much logical connection with the diseased portion of their bodies. In the evenings I would complain to Shelagh as I ate my supper about how a hippopotamus with chronic pneumonia of both lungs had breathed apparently evenly and without difficulty right up to the point of death and had not been heard to cough one single, soft cough. And about how monkeys that I found to be riddled with tuberculosis had played, fought, eaten, mated and harassed their keeper until struck down within the space of five minutes as if smitten by thunderbolts. "It's as if the zoo animals have some tacit conspiracy to give me a hard time," I would ruminate as I tackled my steak pudding and peas. "Maybe Norman Whittle was right. It doesn't make much difference whether I do anything or nothing, the outcome is inevitable."

"Nonsense!" Shelagh would reply. "You've got to learn to walk before you can run. And after all, it was your idea to go in for zoo animals."

With more homilies on the general theme of having to break eggs to make omelettes, she would brew me a mug of coffee and I would go into the lounge to spend an hour or two reading books or journals on exotica. Although there were as yet no books available on zoo medicine, occasional papers were being published here and there by scientists working in Africa, in laboratories and in places such as the mighty San Diego Zoo. For a few minutes in the evenings I could escape from my problems with Belle Vue and Matt Kelly and learn what veterinarians were doing in sunnier climates. Even San Diego, it appeared, did not have it too easy, and the Prosector's Annual Report from London Zoo, a detailed record of the toll of creatures dying from disease and accidental injury, grimly reflected my experience in Manchester. The crying need was still for a range of powerful but safe sedatives and anaesthetics which would enable all of us to examine and treat living exotic creatures more thoroughly. On top of that, we needed a sure way of delivering the drugs to wild and dangerous critters over distances ranging from a few feet to tens of yards. Until we had such weapons in our armoury I would have to go on collecting hair, droppings, urine and other possibly useful stray material from sick animals in the hope of getting enlightenment from the Test (rather like a soothsayer pondering the entrails of a sacrificial chicken), while Matt Kelly stood stolidly by with an expression on his face which said quite clearly that scientific mumbo-jumbo could never take the place of good old-fashioned zooman's know-how.

6

"Not Bad, Young Feller"

One way Matt Kelly demonstrated his inborn zooman's skill brilliantly was in knowing exactly when it was safe to go into a cage or den with a seriously ill animal, even a dangerous one. He had an eye for picking the earliest moment when, providing I did what I was told, I might get away with injecting an ailing lion, lancing an abscess on the butt of a blood-poisoned and uncaring bear or snatching a quick feel of a tigress's swollen belly without losing a limb or my life in the process.

My first such venture was a David-in-the-leopard's-den episode involving a cat that had picked up the miserable running cold symptoms of feline influenza, no doubt from some mundane domestic puss who had wandered through the big cat house at night in search of stray morsels of meat. Feeling and looking just like a human on the first day of an acute attack of 'flu, the leopard lay in his cage, sneezing miserably, drooling ropes of saliva and blinking blearily through inflamed and watery eyes. I was most impressed when Matt produced his keys and unlocked the cage door.

"Oi think we can go in," he said. "Stick close behind me all the time." I nodded. "All the time," Matt repeated as we crept warily through the door and closed it behind us.

The leopard sneezed, snuffled and snorted where he lay in the straw, but appeared not to notice us. "Oi'm goin' to grab his tail," Matt whispered. "Keep behoind me and jab your injection into it." Tail injections in domestic animals are considered to be utterly beyond the pale, but in zoo animals one sometimes has to give thanks for whatever bit of the patient's anatomy the Good Lord provides. I had my syringe and needle full and ready.

Matt walked quietly over to the leopard, with me shadowing him a full six inches behind. Bending slowly down, he picked up the leopard's tail and pulled. The leopard, miserable as he was, just had to react to such provocation. Growling, he dug his claws through the straw into the wooden floor and glared back over his shoulder at his tormentors. Matt continued pulling. "While he's like this, if oi keep pullin', he can't get his head round and into me," he grunted.

Suddenly the grip of the leopard's claws on the floor gave way and the animal skidded back towards us. Angered now, he slewed his front half round and lashed out with his front claws. Matt continued to pull the tail and started to skip backwards. "Oi've got to keep the tail at full stretch," he said more loudly as I skipped backwards too, trying to match my footsteps with his to avoid our legs tangling and both of us tumbling over with an increasingly irate, probably headachy leopard on top.

Back we went and back came the cat. The more he struggled, the faster we went. As we came near a corner, we backed off at an angle. Our strange paso doble, or rather paso triple, continued round the cage. We just could not afford to let the leopard catch up with the end of his tail.

"Roight, now," said Matt eventually, puffing with the exertion of the dance, "reach round me and stick it in!"

It was not easy, tripping energetically backwards, with Matt's bulk blocking my view of the rear half of the spitting

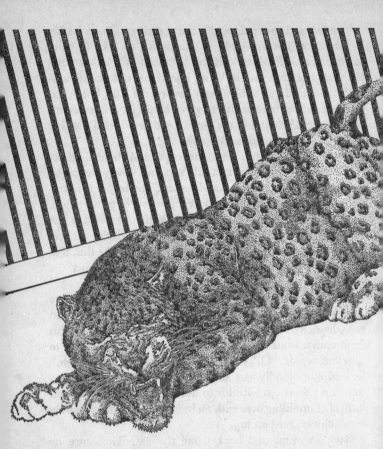

'flu victim, to reach round and stick the hypodermic needle under the skin of the tail. I looked round Matt as we danced, chose my point and thrust forward my syringe. Matt's shoulder obstructed my line of sight again. I prodded blindly towards the position I had chosen. "Bejasus," yelled Matt, "ye've jabbed me hand!"

Startled, I pulled back my needle. Luckily I had not begun depressing the plunger, but the back of Matt's neck had gone the colour of smoked salmon.

"Again, again, try again," he shouted testily, "but for Gawd's sake look where ye're goin'."

Still trotting backwards behind the now-sweating head keeper, I steadied myself with one arm round his waist, craned my neck awkwardly to the right, spotted the tail once more and launched a second attempt. This time I struck home and was greeted by the manhandled leopard with a throaty roar of outrage. "Done," I declared. "What do we do now?"

"Keep goin' till we're next by the door," replied Matt, "then ye back out. Oi'll throw him forwards and follow ye." It was our last circumnavigation of the cage. When I was in position I retreated from the dance floor and crashed with relief through the doorway. With a skilful flick of his strong wrists Matt threw the leopard forward and away from him. Before the animal had time to gather himself for a riposte, Matt had joined me outside the cage and banged the door to.

Puffing, the head keeper wiped his forehead and sucked the red spot on his hand where I had punctured him. "Not bad, young feller," he said, "not bad." I was delighted. That "not bad" from Matt was worth a thousand guineas to me. "But ye'll have to practise your Oswaldtwistle Barn Dance." He reminded me about it the following Christmas when, at the annual Belle Vue party, he took the floor for this English north country dance where partners go three by three. Not a bad dancer, Matt.

My successful injection of the fully conscious savage beast produced a euphoria which was to last all of twenty minutes. Walking back from the big cat house, Matt and I passed the ape house. In the sunlit open-air cage was a fit-looking three-year-old chimp with eyes as bright as buttons.

"Who's that?" I asked the head keeper.

"That's Lee, son of Katja and Robert, a grand little feller."

I stood for a moment to admire the chimpanzees. Lee

seemed positively entranced by me; his eyes never left me. Could it be, I thought in the afterglow of my feat of derring-do with the leopard, that he senses in me something of Dr. Dolittle? Maybe I have got that special way with animals. Lee stared on. True, he did not seem to be quite catching my eye, but there was no doubt that something about me was riveting his attention.

I vaulted the metal barrier designed to stop the public from doing what I was about to do and went closer to the cage. My confidence knew no bounds. Lee continued to gaze adoringly at me but seemed to be fascinated by my chest rather than my face. The reason rapidly became clear as he pushed an arm through the bars of the cage and with a lightning-fast movement snatched at my shirt, an expensive pink one lightly embroidered with glossy whorls in light brown, of which I was rather fond. With one single, precise yank, he pulled the garment clean away from my body. I stood unhurt but dumbfounded, naked from the waist up. In the background the Irishman began to scoff loudly as Lee shuffled off to the back of the cage with his prize and tried it on for size. It was not a very good fit, but that did not seem to bother him at all.

"My shirt," I exclaimed pointlessly. "My shirt."

"Ye've seen the last of that," chuckled Kelly. "All the tea in China couldn't get it away from him; oi've told ye before about goin' close to primate cages." He had. One of the first lessons I had learned when walking along the narrow central corridor that divides the sleeping quarters of Belle Vue's monkey house was to keep dead on the middle line, or grey, brown, black or greenish little arms would snake out and pull my hair, give me a thick ear or steal any detachable object such as fountain pen or stethoscope. Now my shirt was very definitely Lee's. For long after you could still see the remains of it lovingly hoarded in his bed, fragmented and less recognizable, but Lee appeared to treasure it even more than I ever had.

I felt rather exposed setting off home half naked, as Matt grinned and said something to Len, the head ape keeper, about "young boyos with more larnin' than sense".

"Hello, Tarzan," said Shelagh with a giggle as I walked into the kitchen, "tea's ready."

It would be wrong to give the impression that everything I attempted in the zoo fulfilled Matt's gloomy predictions by ending in disaster. Cracked toenails on elephants did well on the hoof oil I prescribed, and I had cleared a llama or two of lice—but Matt Kelly had been getting similar results on zoo animals before I was born. Maybe he had used automobile engine oil on the elephants' feet and simple flowers of sulphur to destroy the llamas' parasites, but they had worked almost as well and nearly as quickly as my up-to-date drugs. To break into the business properly and become a zoo vet in Matt's eyes I would have to do better than that. I consoled myself with the thought that the director, Ray Legge, seemed to appreciate my efforts. Perhaps it was because, as an aquarist, he too was learning in this hotch-potch of a captive jungle.

We learnt together on one emergency which happened on Matt Kelly's day off. Some mindless member of the public had thrown a ball of string over the wire into the big cat enclosure, and a puma had decided to play with it. It was fun! When he tapped it, it rolled along the grass. A thwack from a paw and it spun through the air. The puma pounced on it and gnawed it, pretending it was a rabbit that he had cleverly stalked and finally seized in one irresistible attack. The ball of string began to unravel. The big cat licked idly at the imaginary body of his prey and a loose end of string stuck to his tongue. All cats' tongues have harsh, abrasive upper surfaces on which prickly cells point backwards to help the animal lap up liquids efficiently. The puma continued licking when he felt the string in his mouth, and the movement of his tongue inevitably pushed it farther and farther backwards. Like the incurving fangs of a snake, the scales on the tongue provided a one-way ratchet, making it difficult if not impossible for the creature to spit out what had been taken in. The puma felt the string at the back of his throat and pawed vainly in an effort to dislodge the tickly thread. The string stayed put, so the puma started to lick and swallow to try to put an end to the irritation. The end of the string disappeared. The puma licked and

swallowed. The unravelling ball of string became smaller as inch by inch it crept down the animal's gullet.

Ray Legge telephoned me early in the morning. "Will you come over and look at one of the young pumas? It's an odd case. There's one piece of string hanging out of the mouth and another from the anus."

When I arrived at Belle Vue the position had not changed. Sure enough, the animal had about three inches of string dangling from one end and a slightly smaller length trailing from the other. Ray and I agreed that both bits of string looked very much alike and might well be one and the same piece. The puma was not bothering to lick at the fragment hanging from his lips and appeared perfectly healthy. The possibility that we were looking at two ends of a single piece had ominous undertones. Endless opportunities for trouble in the bowel were offered by such a foreign body. I would have to anaesthetize the animal.

Ray had designed a new cat house with special squeeze compartments where I could get to grips safely with my patients, but it was not easy to entice the animal into the restraining device to give it a shot of anaesthetic. I made a mental note to order one of the new darting pistols that I had just heard were being produced in the United States. At last the puma was immobilized and I gave my anaesthetic. In ten minutes he was sleeping peacefully and we pulled him out into the passageway of the cat house so that I could examine him.

Kneeling down and concentrating on the puma, I made the cardinal error of forgetting about my rear when in a confined space flanked by caged animals. As I bent to give a gentle pull to the string hanging from the puma's jaws, a nearby leopard whipped its forepaw through the bars, dug a hooked claw deeply into my right ankle, anchoring itself behind my Achilles tendon, and tried to haul me into its cage. In agony I tumbled round and literally unpicked the tough hook of nail from my bleeding leg. Thank goodness Matt isn't here, was all I could think, I've fumbled it again.

Pausing to stick some of the penicillin cream normally used up cows' udders into my wound and bind it with gauze, I returned my attentions to the puma. Tugging the string at either end did not budge it a millimetre. I decided that it might not be wise to pull really hard; I was not sure why, but I felt that if the string did not slip conveniently out the force might do untold damage to the animal's insides. Besides, I still could not be certain that the two portions were not separate. "I'll have to open him up," I told Ray. "I'll go into the abdomen first to find out how far the string extends and then maybe open the intestines."

We carried the unconscious big cat on a wheelbarrow over to the dispensary and the operation was soon under way. I inspected the loops of bowel. Sure enough, I could feel the firm thread of string running right through the animal's alimentary canal.

"My hands are sterile—will you try pulling the string at the back end, Ray?" I asked. The zoo director pulled lightly at the puma's rear beyond the draped operation sheets, while I watched the effect on the exposed bowel loops. When Ray pulled, the intestines began to concertina together as if he were drawing the cord on a pair of unoccupied pyjamas. I told him to stop pulling at once. Any more of that and the string would begin to cut into the delicate folded lining of the bowel tube. Thank God I had not tried brute force in extracting the string—it would have sliced open the intestines at a couple of dozen points. There was only one way. At six places between the duodenum and rectum I had to pierce the intestine wall, fish in for the string, cut it and then sew up the wall with waterproof stitching. At every second incision I pulled out the freed section of string after cutting it.

An hour later it was completed. The puma had six patches in his food canal and I had all the string. With his abdomen sewn up and pumped full of antibiotics to prevent peritonitis, the still-sleeping puma was wheeled back to his night house.

"Marvellous job," said Ray, patting me on the back, "really worthwhile." Pity old Kelly wasn't there, I thought. Telling him tomorrow won't have the impact of the real thing.

Ten days later I took the stitches out of the recovered puma with Matt helping me to give the anaesthetic. "You ought to have seen it, Matt," I said proudly. "String from end to end like a bunch of black puddings. Good thing I operated."

Matt nodded and spat accurately at a drain. "Pumas," he said, "pumas. Sure, they're a drug on the market. Dime a dozen these days. Makes me wonder if they're worth spendin' money on."

Despite Matt's scepticism, my experience was beginning to extend beyond split toenails and lousy llamas. If there was the slightest chance of saving an animal's life Ray and I took it, and Matt was roped in to help as I fitted a custom-built wooden leg, complete with ingenious articulated foot, to a flamingo whose limb I had amputated because of gangrene; he held the bowl of water while I took casts of a newborn zebra foal's neck which had been bitten and broken by its father shortly after birth, and for which I designed a glass fibre support to keep the foal's head up while the bones healed. Times were gradually changing, and a major turning-point came the day I received through the post from America my gas-powered dart-gun. What was more the drug company, Parke, Davis, had sent me a supply of a promising new drug, phencyclidine, to try out on zoo animals. Concentrated enough to be used in the dart-gun syringes, and said to be fast-acting, it gave me a new optimism about my future as a zoo vet.

I took my new toys over to Belle Vue to show Ray, but he was not in his office so I drove through the grounds to the animal kitchen. Walking into the room where the diets are made up, I found Matt standing at the sink shaving. The foamy lather from his face was dropping onto a tray of frozen sprats that were being thawed out for the penguins.

"Dear me, Mr. Kelly," I said sternly, "what are you doing? It's hardly the right thing to do one's ablutions all over the animal food. The practice will have to stop at once."

The stocky Irishman glared at me like an apoplectic Father Christmas, blew a few soapy bubbles but said nothing. He began rinsing the sprats. I went out, leaving the crestfallen Matt with half his beard still on. I grinned to myself when I was out of sight. A belated comeback, I thought; one point to me.

Now that I had a dart-gun and the new drug, I was all set to break for ever with the old days of impotent guesswork from the other side of the bars or the opposite bank of the moat. The use of tranquillizers in the food of zoo animals had not proved to be very reliable—most of the drugs then available were designed for humans and did not necessarily work on wild beasts. Anyway, the animals could not be guaranteed to take the pills ground up and mixed with their food, and if they did the stuff often got lost among the vast quantities of digesting material churning around in their stomachs and either produced no signs of sleepiness or did so hours later when we were long gone and in bed. The doses of human tranquillizers also had to be multiplied many times when administered to exotic animals, even small ones, and the thousands of pills that would be required for a biggy like an elephant made the whole business farcical. Ray Legge and I had also tried jabbing injections of dope into awkward animals like giraffe with syringes attached to the end of long poles, but it never really worked. We just broke a lot of needles and even more poles.

The first animals on which I tried my gun and phencyclidine were some wolves that Ray wanted to move from one lot of quarters to another within the zoo. Nervously I loaded a dozen darts and then, one after the other, fired them at the prowling animals. Plop, plop, plop. I learned how easy it was to hit shoulder, thigh or neck muscle. Within ten minutes all the wolves were asleep—we had never seen anything like it. The whole transfer was completed within half an hour. I went on to lions and then bears. Never a hitch, never a fatality. The drug was ideal on monkeys, chimps, gorillas. It kept the animals unconscious for about an hour and then wore off gradually over the next day or so.

Phencyclidine appeared to be the universal bringer of dreams I had been seeking.

Then I hit the first snags. I lost my first elephant, Mary, after a long operation to remove a tooth with a root abscess; the prolonged period of recovery from phencyclidine in such a large creature resulted in fatal congestion of the lungs. I experimented on zebras needing emergency suturing of wounds. The phencyclidine put the animals down but the nightmares they seemed to experience, and the hours of frantic crashing about as the chemical faded slowly from their systems, were painful to witness. After one awful night spent with Matt Kelly in a straw-smothered loose box, soothing and struggling to hold down a lathered, wild-eyed zebra stallion that was coming round from phencyclidine anaesthesia, I vowed never to use the drug again on equines. Fortunately, two newer drugs, xylazine and etorphine, would soon appear and prove the answer to doping zebra.

Although phencyclidine was first-class in bears, the polar bear was more sensitive to it than its cousins were and needed a much smaller dose to knock it out. It was my success in anaesthetizing polar bears at Belle Vue which led to my first piece of circus work. Billy Smart's Circus was at Prestwick in Scotland and had a male polar bear with the irritating condition common in these deceptive and highly dangerous creatures, ulceration between the toes. Polar bears have lots of fur on their feet to insulate them against the cold of ice and snow, but in captivity it often becomes matted between their toes into hard little balls. The balls act as foreign bodies and rub uncomfortably at the soft flesh on either side of them. Gradually ulcers are formed which attract fungus and other types of infection, and the accumulated hair balls must be cut out. The Smarts and I had met at the circus held every Christmas at Belle Vue, and they asked me to go up to Prestwick to dope the bear and clean up his feet.

I felt wildly elated as I drove back down from Scotland after darting in the phencyclidine and then taking my scissors and soothing ointments to the massive paws of the slumbering white giant. Zoo work is one thing; impressing the hard-bitten animal men of the circus world, who tend to have firm prejudices about veterinary matters, is another thing altogether. The Smarts had seemed very impressed with my fast, no-nonsense anaesthesia.

The gun and the new drugs could be the key to bringing veterinary help to circus animals as well, then, but the next patient on which I used it was back at Belle Vue. One morning Matt Kelly telephoned in a terrible flap; Ray Legge was away on holiday and he was acting zoo director. He sounded desperate yet resigned. "Get down as soon as ye can, Doctor. It's an oryx cow. She's just calved and all her insoides are hangin' out. It looks very bad."

Listening to Matt's brief description I could guess what had happened, but I did not waste time telling him about it over the telephone. I told him to keep the animal quiet, to cover the "insoides" with a clean, moist sheet to keep them from becoming damaged or dirty, and to wait for me. Then I jumped into my car and set off for Manchester.

Matt's face was long and sombre as I walked into the oryx shed. I had never seen him looking so downcast. He did not bother to greet me but just announced bleakly, "She's had it. No question. Oi've never seen such a mess in all me years as a zoo keeper."

The Beisa oryx was lying on her side on a pile of straw, her hind quarters draped in white sheeting stained with large fuzzy shadows of red. Under the sheet a bloody pink balloon of flesh, studded with purple cherry-like objects and as big as the animal's head and neck, lay on the straw. It was attached by a narrow neck to the vulva. As I had guessed, the oryx had calved and discharged the afterbirth; then the whole of the womb, with the ovaries attached, had turned inside out and fallen through the pelvis into the fresh air. The oryx's entire womb and associated structures had prolapsed and were lying on the ground for all to see.

"Just look at her," continued Matt. "She's had it, oi can tell ye that. No animal can survoive havin' all its insoides turned out. Fancy drugs and such can't help her!" He clicked his teeth agitatedly.

Uterine prolapse is fairly common in sheep and cattle and occasionally occurs spectacularly in sows. It is rarely seen in wild animals. This was the first time Matt or I had come across it in the zoo, but unlike him I knew what it was and had wrestled with many similar cases in farm animals. I decided to keep that to myself for the moment. "Get some warm water and plenty of towels," I instructed. Matt went out sighing.

As I went towards the oryx's head to examine her, she threatened me with her wicked straight horns which I had seen driven with accuracy through two-inch wood planking. I would have to dope her before tackling her hind end, although I could not be sure what the effect of phencyclidine would be on her four-stomach digestion. Matt watched while I also injected 10 cc of local anaesthetic to paralyse her spinal cord and stop her straining by reflex action when I began to work. Next I thoroughly washed the exposed lining of the womb and its "cherries", which were the attachment points of the calf's placenta, and picked off bits of straw and grime. "Now then, Matt," I said when it was clean, "I want you to put a towelling sling under the womb and hold it clear of the ground to stop it getting dirty again."

He took a towel, looped it under the flabby mess of raw flesh and lifted it off the straw. I coated the womb liberally with a sulphonamide antiseptic cream. Now for the tough bit. As the womb had fallen inside out, I had to replace it gently but firmly by rolling it inwards from the centre as if it were a plastic bag or woollen sock that was inside out. Womb walls are thick and spongy but easily punctured by too rough fingers, so I had to be extremely careful to use only the balls of my fingertips. Bit by bit the womb began to fold inwards. I kept lubricating it with obstetric cream. The size of the exposed womb began to decrease as I worked away with both arms groping in the oryx's pelvic canal.

Matt said nothing as he strained to hold the towelling up, and I knelt below him, concentrating, with my tongue stuck between my lips. At last, with a satisfying sucking noise, the last bit of the womb disappeared inside the vulva. I pushed it well forward inside the animal. Luckily I have a long arm with a smallish hand, ideal for this sort of obstetrical problem.

"Get me a milk bottle, Matt," I said finally.

The head keeper broke his silence. "A milk bottle? What for?"

"Get it please, and quick!" I replied sternly.

Matt dropped the towel and disappeared again. He came back with a milk bottle which, while he watched curiously, I disinfected with iodine soap. Then to his amazement I plunged my arm back inside the oryx's womb with the bottle held firmly by the neck. Using its blunt bottom as an extension to my arm, I made sure that the part of the womb beyond the reach of my fingers was folded back into its proper position. If I did not do that, the thing would be out again in no time. Withdrawing the milk bottle and still not explaining its function, or what indeed the whole business had been about, I finished off by putting a few clips into the vulva as a precaution. I would remove them after thirty-six hours. Done. The animal's colour, pulse and respiration were good.

I scrubbed my hands and arms and then turned to Matt. "She'll be right as a clock by tonight," I said. "It was just a prolapsed uterus."

Matt stared at the clean and tidy hind end of the oryx and cleared his throat. "Incredible," he said at last. "Incredible. The foinest bit of work oi've ever seen in all me years. Oi take me hat off, Dr. Taylor."

That was some reward, coming from Matt. Better still, just as I had predicted, by evening the oryx was indeed as good as new, and I tried hard not to gloat as Matt and I stood watching her suckle her lusty calf.

The disease problems of primates, apes and monkeys, had always fascinated me, so I was stung by a remark by Ray Legge that medical doctors were by tradition more equipped to deal with such animals than veterinarians. I decided to embark on a study course in an attempt to prove him wrong and in the process to gain a Fellowship of the Royal College of Veterinary Surgeons. After a year and a half's hard work, sandwiching the studies in where I could between my day-to-day clinical work and attending postgraduate courses at the medical school in Manchester, I got my Fellowship, the first ever given where zoo animals were named as the speciality. Not only did my practice with great apes in particular now have a firm base, but through the study I had had to do at home for the Fellowship Shelagh was becoming increasingly involved with some of my simian patients.

Soon after I gained my Fellowship, Jane, a charming female orang-utan at Belle Vue, was pregnant for the first time. Then, with about two months still to go before her time was due, she suddenly had a miscarriage. A premature scrap of an orang infant was born dead one night.

The effect on Jane was remarkable and profound. All the other female orangs had live, healthy babies. She sat alone in a corner hugging the shrivelled corpse of her baby, trying in vain to make it suckle and whimpering in distress. I am not a sentimentalist prone to seeing the whole range of human emotions in animals, but when I first saw Jane after the miscarriage, I felt tears in my eyes. She was heartbroken. Try as we might we could not get her to give up the baby's body. I began to consider darting her with a sedative in order to remove it before it putrefied further. The distraught female would not touch food and she began to lose weight alarmingly.

I took Shelagh with me to the zoo when I finally decided to knock Jane out and take the infant cadaver. We went into the isolation room where Jane sat pitifully in a large cage. Shelagh looked at the orang and the orang looked at her. I saw her eyes fill. Matt and I stood silently.

"Before you try darting," said Shelagh suddenly, "I want to go in with her."

My wife was asking to go in with a full-grown orang that was undoubtedly in a disturbed and unpredictable mood.

"I mean it," she said. "Open the door please, Mr. Kelly."

Matt started to speak but I interrupted him. "OK," I said. "Open it, Matt."

Matt undid the lock and cautiously swung open the barred door. Shelagh climbed into the cage and on hands and knees crawled straight over to Jane. When she reached the orang, she at once began talking to the animal in soothing low tones. "What's the matter, love?" she murmured. "I know all about it. Come on, put an arm round me." On and on she talked, with the orang looking straight into her face. Shelagh sat down beside Jane and gave her a cuddle that was full of love and understanding. To our delight and astonishment, Jane snuggled into her and put her broad lips to Shelagh's mouth. Shelagh stroked Jane's hair and kept up the flow of sympathetic talk. Then, just like that, Jane gave Shelagh the dead orang. Shelagh took it, cradled it, talked admiringly about it, then slowly slipped it into one of her pockets. Jane did not make one gesture of protest.

"Pass me some food," Shelagh said to us. We handed in some bananas and grapes. Shelagh took them, broke them into portions and presented them to the orang's mouth. Jane took them one by one.

"I'd like to give her a stimulant, Shelagh," I said quietly. "I'll come in too."

"No, you won't," she replied. "Fill your syringe, tell me where to put it and I'll do it—won't I, Jane dear?"

"But Mrs. Taylor," Matt remonstrated, "she'll boite. Oi think we'd . . ."

Shelagh was having none of it. Reluctantly I made up a syringe and passed it in to my wife. "In the thigh muscle," I instructed. Cooing to her friend, with one arm still hugging her, Shelagh slipped the needle into Jane's leg. She did not budge a millimetre.

After a while, Shelagh left the cage and gave us the little

corpse. Jane was no longer whimpering. She looked more tranquil as she watched my wife close the door. "I'll be in again tomorrow," said Shelagh briskly to Matt and me. She had taken over.

And that is how it was. Every day Shelagh went in with Jane, feeding her by hand, talking to her just like women do to their girl friends, particularly when they have suffered some misfortune, and giving her lots of loving cuddles. Jane responded. She began to cuddle Shelagh in return and stopped losing weight. Gradually she started to feed herself again. In three weeks she appeared completely normal.

I am certain that the injections that Shelagh gave sitting cheek by jowl with a great ape that could have broken every bone in her body did not play much part in Jane's recovery. As Shelagh said, "There are some things in zoo work that just can't be left to men."

7
Widening Horizons

I had landed the practice with a thumping big bad debt, and
Norman Whittle was not amused. After chasing about for
several weeks treating a touring circus's arthritic elephant
with injections of gold salts, I found the circus had done the
dirty on me. Its owner claimed that the animal rightfully
belonged to such and such a clown, who in turn maintained
that I had originally been called in by one of a family of
acrobats while the circus was in Rochdale. The company
was a small one, everyone seemed to be interrelated and the
clowns doubled or even trebled as ice-cream sellers, bareback
riders or jugglers. Trying to get my fee out of anyone was
futile and embarrassing. If I called during a performance
everyone was dashing round concealed under greasepaint
and tomato-sized rubber noses, and at other times the trailers
were silent as the grave when I knocked miserably on the
doors for my cash. Strange, when the elephant had been
creaking painfully about on puffy, tense joints, I had been
able to find the staff in a trice in order to make my examina-
tions. But gradually the circus moved farther and farther
away from Rochdale and debt-collecting forays became
impossible.

The bad debt led to a bitter exchange with Norman of
the sort that made me long to make the great leap and to
throw in my lot with wild-animal medicine lock, stock and
barrel.

"Apart from the time you've spent gallivanting all over England away from the practice," Norman said in his undemonstrative, clipped manner as we stood over the unconscious body of a tortoiseshell cat on which we were doing a hysterectomy, "we're over a hundred quid out of pocket. This circus farce can't go on. Anyway you can't trust travelling folk, fly-by-nights, gipsies. I warned you time and again. And even if they had paid, look at all the time and effort and driving. Compare that to work like this." He waved a needle holder at the supine she-cat. "Thirty shillings, nearly all profit and done in five minutes!"

Looked at from a purely financial point of view, it was true; one vet we both knew frequently said that his ideal practice would consist of doing nothing but sterilizing she-cats, six in the morning and six in the afternoon. But that was not my view of veterinary work. Could they not see that taking the pulse of an elephant, feeling the thick artery deep under the dry, crinkly skin, was a reward in itself? Cash cannot be equated with seeing a cub in its foetal membranes emerge like a vacuum-packed pigeon, especially if you have helped it out. Even more especially if, as you peel the membranes from it, it writhes and natters the first feeble protest of its independent life. No, I felt as strongly then as I do now that it was a rare privilege to be allowed to try to heal wild living organisms. Can a stockbroker or banker know anything of the happiness which I have had when seeing a leg walk that I, somehow, have helped tack together?

I had talked before in this vein to Norman, but decided it would be pointless to start again this time. I think he thought I would grow out of it, so he was exasperated by my enthusiastic acceptance of our next circus call. It was from an outfit completely unknown to us at Great Yarmouth, two hundred miles or more away across country on the coast of the wind-washed fens of Norfolk. Again the problem was an elephant, an elephant suspected of foot-and-mouth disease.

"You can't go off down there," said my partner angrily. "This zoo and circus work is getting too much. No, we just can't have it."

An elephant with suspected foot-and-mouth? Nothing could stop me. "I'm off," I said, and slipped out of the door before he could say another word.

It was a long drive that took nearly six hours. By now I was receiving calls to exotic animals from all over Britain as the knowledge that I had a special interest in such creatures spread by word of mouth from one owner to another. My mileage was increasing rapidly, and on long journeys I was troubled by being out of contact with my surgery and the rest of the world for most of the day. Anything could be happening while I was doing nothing but acting as taxi driver to myself. To remedy this I had recently done something which was to prove the key to roving zoo practice: I had installed in the car a radio telephone operating on a private network that extended virtually all over the country. My call sign was the zippy "Jet eight-seven" and I got a great kick from receiving messages on the road like the first one that came over the air from Belle Vue: "Calling Jet eight-seven, Jet eight-seven. Mr. Kelly reports pigmy hippo born. All well. Repeat, all well. Over."

I had plenty to ponder as I crossed the flat marshes of East Anglia. There were the problems with Norman and my role in the practice: I owed Norman a lot for introducing me to zoo work, and I could understand his frustration at being left to cope on his own so much, but I knew that my first duty was to the animals I was trying to help. Then foot-and-mouth disease. I had never seen a real live case. As for such a thing in elephants, I had heard of a few suspect cases where large ulcers had formed at the back of the mouth, but that was all I knew apart from the fact that no foot-and-mouth disease was being reported in Britain at that time. There must be some likelier explanation.

At last I rolled into Great Yarmouth, a place exactly like

dozens of other holiday towns dotted round the English coast, redolent with the faded fashion of Victorian and Regency days when Majorca and the Costa Brava were as far away as the moon. The circus was inside the Hippodrome Theatre, and I soon found the elephant lines. Near three adult female Indian elephants an old lugubrious-faced German, who turned out to be the elephant trainer, a midget in a Charlie Chaplin outfit, a policeman and another man in a black rubber coat and gumboots were arguing. The midget seemed particularly agitated.

I went over. "I'm Dr. Taylor to see the elephant."

The man in the rubber coat put out a hand. "Tompkins," he said, "Ministry of Agriculture vet. Came out to see what this report of F-and-M was all about."

"And they won't pay me my half-crown," squeaked the midget, tapping me on the knee. "I want my half-crown."

"I am Herr Hopfer," said the German. "Please, Doktor, come zis way. Gerda iss very ill." He looked as if he was about to burst into tears.

"My half-crown! It's the rule! My half-crown!" The midget was fairly hopping about by this time and was waving his miniature bent walking-stick at the policeman.

The latter cleared his throat and sighed. He had obviously been saying something similar for the past half-hour. "I 'ave told you once, Mr. Lemon, and I 'ave told you twice. I know nothin' about no 'alf-crown. You'll 'ave to go down to the station and see my sergeant about that."

"What's this all about?" I asked Tompkins.

"Oh, it's all because he, Mr. Lemon, reported the suspect case of F-and-M. Apparently there's something in the law that says if any private citizen suspects a notifiable disease in anybody's animal, whether he knows what he's looking at or not, he can claim two-and-sixpence from the police."

"Is that right?" I queried.

"Can't say I know anything about it, but the little fellow's mad as hell on getting his cash. Claims to know all about it."

"Done my duty, done my duty! Where's my half-crown?" The midget started buzzing again.

"Now look 'ere, Mr. Lemon," said the policeman.

"Just give me the money," yelled Mr. Lemon.

Tompkins and I looked silently at one another and simultaneously put our hands in our pockets. We produced one-and-threepence each and pushed the coins at the midget. "Now can we please have some hush while we look at the bloody elephant!" I said tetchily.

Mr. Lemon waddled off, and later I learned that he was quite right; he was indeed entitled to the reward whatever the diagnosis turned out to be.

Gerda the elephant was standing miserably in a pool of water which streamed slowly from her lower lip to the cobbled floor. The water was her own saliva. I must look inside her mouth at once, but Matt Kelly had warned me of the danger of sticking one's hand blindly into an elephant's mouth: "If the craytchure moves her lower jaw, ye've a pulverized hand."

"Get her to open up, Herr Hopfer," I said. It is one thing all elephant trainers can do with their animals.

"Gerda, auf, auf!" he shouted.

Gerda slowly raised her trunk and opened her soft pink mouth. Tompkins shone his torch in and we both peered into the narrow space between the teeth. Not a blister or an ulcer in sight.

"I don't think elephants can get F-and-M," said Tompkins. "Better check her feet, though, just in case."

He walked cautiously round the elephant, looking at her neatly filed and oiled toenails. Nothing that looked like ulcers there. Tompkins was shining his light on the left rear foot when Gerda felt the urge to pass water. Unwisely, the ministry vet was not wearing the Government-issue black sou'wester that is supposed to be part of the uniform for investigations into notifiable disease. He took the cataract square on top of his head. It went down the inside of his coat and ran out below.

"I 'ave 'eard that yoorine is very good for the complexion," observed the policeman, as deadpan as if he were making an arrest.

"I'm off," spluttered Tompkins. "Negative F-and-M here. End of the affair as far as the Ministry's concerned. Get on with it, Taylor." Spitting, he squelched away.

"Now, Herr Hopfer," I said, "tell me the full story."

"Zis morning I find her streaming from ze mouss like zis. She vill not eat, not even drink. Maybe she hass a bad tooss."

Toothache was indeed a possibility. One of the commonest ailments in elephants is an infected or badly positioned molar. I got Hopfer to make Gerda open her mouth again and shone my torch carefully on each tooth with one hand while pressing down the slippery ball of her tongue with the other. One slip and I could lose a finger or three. All the teeth seemed normal. I felt Gerda's glands, ran my hands down over the outside of her throat, took her temperature and drew a blood sample. Everything was OK. But Gerda was miserable and would not eat or drink, and her saliva ran and ran. There was no evidence that her throat was inflamed, her swallowing muscles were not paralysed, there was no logical reason why she should be producing excessive quantities of saliva. I was left with one ominous probability.

"Bring me some bananas and a bucket of water," I said to Hopfer. I wanted to watch her reaction to food very carefully for myself. Treating elephants was not much different from treating cattle, I was finding, as long as you knew how to handle them and how to love them.

When the elephant trainer returned, I presented Gerda with a peeled banana. She took it with her trunk tip, popped it in her mouth and swallowed readily. Then slowly, slowly, the pulped banana came back and dripped in sticky blobs from the corners of her lips. I put the bucket of water in front of her. Immediately she sucked up a trunkful and squirted it into her mouth. She swallowed. For a moment nothing happened and then the water gushed back out onto the floor.

"What did you feed the elephants last thing yesterday, Herr Hopfer?"

"Chopped carrots and apples."

"Chopped?"

"Ja, chopped."

I was certain now that one of the apples had evaded the chopper's cleaver and was jammed somewhere in the gullet. And I could predict that it would be in one of three places: where the gullet enters the chest, where it passes over the heart or where it pierces the diaphragm. Wherever it was, Gerda was in big trouble.

In cattle, similar jammed objects often pass naturally if the animal is left alone for twenty-four hours. That was my first feeble line of attack. I booked in at a nearby hotel and made sure that the hungry and thirsty elephant at least had plenty of water to suck up. Maybe a trickle would get past the apple, I thought optimistically as I added nourishing glucose to the water. The next day, Gerda was much worse. She was sunken-eyed, weak and obviously dehydrated. How to move the apple? If I pushed it somehow, I could rupture the oesophagus. Operating was out of the question; no machine could keep the six-ton monster's lungs inflated with oxygen when the chest cavity was opened. Drugs designed to relax the muscles of the gullet had no effect.

By the third day the poor elephant was so weak that she could almost be pushed off balance by one man. Her eyes were red and her breath was foul. The apple was still firmly lodged and the river of saliva flowed on. Gerda was now desperately thirsty. Stripped down to my underpants, I started a series of hourly enemas, trying to pump water and glucose as far as possible into her lower bowel with a plastic tube and an old stirrup pump borrowed from the Hippodrome's fire-fighting equipment. It was slow, dirty work.

"Ooh!" said the waitress in my hotel when she learnt

that I was working at the circus. "What a super job. Lovely animals and able to have a holiday by the seaside at the same time!"

She should have been there all night, pumping ten gallons of sugary water up an elephant's backside and getting nine gallons sprayed back over her, I thought, as the waitress flounced off for my pot of tea and kippered herrings. Still, it had been worth it. A gallon had stayed up, a gallon that might just keep Gerda going till something turned up.

On the fifth day I had to make a crucial decision. The elephant was deteriorating rapidly. The only thing left was to push a probe down her throat. This meant anaesthesia. By now Gerda was unwilling to lie down for fear of being unable to rise. Left much longer, she would not tolerate doping, for lack of sleep had now been added to starvation and thirst and debility.

I walked along the shingly beach and thought long and hard. I considered phoning Norman but, remembering the coolness between us, decided against it. The seagulls chivvied me in the cold, grey sky with incomprehensible advice. For a moment I envied the fishermen sitting muffled on the end of the pier, sucking contented pipes and off home soon to baked beans and TV. Then I decided. I would dope Gerda lightly, pass a probang, a long leather tube with a bulbous brass end, down her gullet and take her life in my inexperienced hands.

Later that day I gave the elephant a massive dose of acetylpromazine, a strong sedative rather than a true anaesthetic. After half an hour she slowly sank to the ground and lay, still drooling, on her side. Herr Hopfer pulled the upper jaw and the diminutive Mr. Lemon, who like most midgets was immensely strong for his size, tugged on the lower. Greasing the probang with cod-liver oil, I pushed it carefully to the back of Gerda's throat. When a couple of feet of tube had disappeared, I stopped and went to the end of the probang outside the elephant and put it to my ear. I could feel no puff of air as Gerda breathed, so at least I was not going the wrong way, down the windpipe. I pushed the probang on slowly. Suddenly it stopped; it would go no farther. I marked the tube and withdrew it so that by measuring it over the outside of the elephant's body I could tell exactly how far down the obstruction lay. The mark on the tube told me that the apple was jammed at the point where the oesophagus passes the great heart. I must push it on. I re-introduced the probang and arrived once more at the obstruction. The moment had arrived. The next strong shove could stop the heart. It could burst the gullet and send the apple into the chest cavity. Or it could succeed. I gritted my teeth and steadily increased pressure on the probang. All at once it began to move freely once more. Something had given. I was sweating and my lip was bleeding where I had bitten it. Had the apple moved on or was it now bobbing around on the lungs with a ragged, gaping hole in the gullet beside it? Through my stethoscope I could hear no ugly noises from the lungs. Hardly daring to breathe, I slowly withdrew the probang. After what seemed an hour, its gleaming brass end flopped out of Gerda's mouth. It was coated in clear slime and shreds of banana pulp but not one drop of blood. I had done it!

Gerda was drowsy for many hours as the sedative wore off. The waiting was intolerable. I went to the cinema but came out after five minutes. I did not feel like eating or drinking. I ran along the beach. I played the one-armed bandits on the pier. Every half-hour I was back at the Hippodrome. At last, at nine o'clock that night, Gerda regained enough energy to rise groggily to her feet.

"Don't do a thing, Herr Hopfer!" I shouted. "I'll do this."

I took a bucket of hay tea, an infusion of hot water and new meadow hay, and placed it in front of Gerda. Her trunk flapped weakly. I grabbed it and stuck it into the golden liquid. The bucket half emptied. Gerda's slow and unsteady trunk curled towards her mouth and injected its contents.

I saw the gullet muscles contract. A wave passed down her throat. She had swallowed. We waited, frozen like statues. The hay tea did not come back. Gerda's trunk was already back in the bucket, draining it dry.

"A banana, a banana!" I shouted excitedly.

The German ran for a bunch of fruit and handed it to me. I stuffed one straight into the elephant's jaws without peeling it. Squelch! It was gone. Nothing drooled back. The ropes of saliva no longer hung from Gerda's bottom lip. Her sunken red eye was on the remainder of the bunch of bananas. A perfect lady, and anyway still appallingly weak, she reached delicately for them. We were on our way.

That night I stayed up with Gerda again, making sure that she was not overloaded too suddenly with food or water, but gradually building up her much-needed intake. By daybreak she was visibly much stronger and the signs of dehydration were disappearing fast. I went back to my hotel when Herr Hopfer woke and relieved me.

"Ooh!" said the waitress as I slumped into my chair at the breakfast table. "Been out on the town, eh? Naughty boy! Told you you'd have a smashin' time at Great Yarmouth. Must be all play, your job."

"Yes," I said wearily. "Bring me an extra pair of kippers, will you? I'm celebrating."

On my return from Great Yarmouth Norman tackled me again about my travels round the country in pursuit of exotic patients. "Anyway," he said, "can you really square your conscience with being involved in zoo and circus animal work? Aren't you just part of the shady business of exploiting wild creatures?"

It is a question people often ask me and from time to time, as I lie in bed, I ask it myself, just to make sure that the answer I give is still the same one, the one I believe in.

I believe in zoos, marinelands, safari parks. To come into close contact with the creatures of the earth—to see, to smell and, if you are lucky enough, to touch the beasts—is a vital part of human experience. Just as cinema cannot catch the atmosphere of the live stage, films of elephants or lions or buffaloes cannot give that spark of magic which flesh-and-blood presence provides. To be snuffled over by the damp tip of an elephant's trunk, to have one's hair lifted by the curling rasp of a giraffe's tongue—out of such experiences spring real feeling and love for fellow animals. There is nothing more rewarding than escorting a group of blind people round a zoo. They truly appreciate, in every sense of the word, camels, puma cubs, snakes, ostriches and the rest of the species to which I feel it is safe to introduce them.

It is pie in the sky to talk of us all going to see the wild animals in their natural habitats. The habitats are shrinking fast, not least because of tourism. The cruel impact of man on animals' natural homes will inevitably lead to more and more birds, mammals, fish and insects becoming extinct in the wild. Wilful greed and careless pollution are taking a terrible toll, and zoos and marinelands have a real part to play in helping at least some creatures to avoid the fate of the dodo, the Steller's sea cow and the quagga. No, zoos are essential for all the kids in New York, London, Rome and a thousand other cities who will never in a million years get the chance to go on a jet-set safari to the Serengeti.

As for me, my job is to represent the animals' interests, to see their point of view. There are disgraceful black spots, disgusting examples of cruelty, neglect and naked exploitation, in animal trapping, zoos, circuses and laboratories in all parts of the world. But by working from the inside, by encouraging breeding here and improving diets there, by trying to heal the sick animals, educating their ignorant owners and proving to them that cruelty and neglect are counter-productive purely in terms of cash, I know things are slowly but steadily getting better. I am proud to be part of it.

When I explained how I felt to Norman, he grunted and

said that was all very well, but how was he expected to run a two-man practice when one of the partners was never there? I wondered what he would say if he knew that I had just received my first call abroad, to go over to Holland the following weekend to inspect and then accompany six young African elephants to England. Since it was Norman's duty weekend anyway, I thought it would be more prudent just to go, and to tell him about it when I got back.

I made the tedious journey by truck and ferry. After the truck had burnt its brakes out and hours had been wasted finding a replacement, I eventually got my charges onto the Rotterdam–Hull overnight boat. I sat alone during the crossing, guarding the elephants and feeding them from time to time with hay, bananas and apples. It was further invaluable experience in animal handling and transportation.

One of my jobs was to keep curious passengers and crew from interfering with the elephants. All went well until the middle of the night when, tired out by the day's exertions, I was unable to keep my eyelids open any longer. Fighting against it, I finally fell asleep propped up in a sitting position against one of the elephant crates.

Three hours later I woke to find that some misguided animal lover had fed my entire stock of apples and bananas to the ever-willing beasts. So much fruit in so short a time could cause six elephantine cases of colic before we docked, and I prepared for the worst. Luckily colic did not develop, but the surfeit of fruit certainly made its presence felt. After half a day spent ministering to a handful of elephants with acute diarrhoea, I knew a little of what it must have been like to be a bell-carrying leper in the Middle Ages, and when I got home Shelagh made me strip down to my underclothes outside the back door.

A few weeks later I was back in Holland, to capture Mr. van den Baars's onagers, and soon after that I took a much longer trip. Its purpose was not to treat any one case but to learn more about one great group of wild mammals of which I still had no experience. These creatures, taking their name from the Greek word for sea monster, second in intelligence only to man himself and descended from insignificant pig-like foragers that rooted around marshy land millions of years ago, were the cetaceans: whales, dolphins and porpoises. In the mid-sixties dolphins became the most fashionable and popular of zoo animals in America. Then Flipper and his relatives came to Europe, and I decided that it was time for me to start learning something about the care and medicine of these beautiful but mysterious beasts. I suspected that marinelands and dolphinaria were going to mushroom in Britain and on the Continent, and that dolphin doctoring was going to become an established branch of the veterinary art.

Today we know more about the dolphin than about any other animal except man and the dog, yet little more than a dozen years ago virtually nothing was known and still less published about cetacean disease. It was uniquely challenging, for this was not a case of trying out horse techniques in zebras or cattle medicine in buffaloes. Cetaceans do not abide by the rules. They have reconquered the watery places of the earth by adapting to a marine existence all the benefits of being a mammal, and combining that with ingenuity in doing things that mammals out at sea would not be expected to do. For that they have to be different: different in body structure, function and behaviour. The Atlantic bottle-nosed dolphin is an air-breathing, warm-blooded animal with three stomachs like a cow's, kidneys like a camel's, a brain as big as a man's, the swimming skills of a shark and the sonar equipment of a bat. It can dive deep and ascend fast without fear of decompression illnesses, endure long periods without oxygen but ignore levels of carbon dioxide that would black out other beasts, and drink nothing but sea water, the brine which drives thirsty casta-ways mad, and it has a bundle of other feats of mystery and imagination at its command.

Only the handful of veterinarians working full time with marine mammals in the United States had the knowledge I would need if I was to treat cetaceans effectively. Leaving the long-suffering Norman in sole charge of the practice once again, and digging deep into my personal savings, I went first to Point Mugu in California, where the U.S. Navy Undersea Warfare Division had a small but high-powered veterinary team led by Dr. Sam Ridgway. Among their research pools and complex of laboratories set on the shore of the Pacific, I embarked on a crash course of sea-going veterinary medicine. Apart from the very different surroundings, it was rather like my first months at Belle Vue under the thumb of Matt Kelly. I learned that dolphins can contract influenza, mumps, polio and gastric ulcers, that their anatomical and physiological adaptations make them the safest creatures in the world to pass a stomach tube on but the most tricky to anaesthetize, and that they require each day three hundred times more Vitamin B_1 than a human of the same weight. An apparently simple thing but most vital of all, I was given my first opportunity to take blood samples from the animals. The smooth, shining skin of a dolphin betrays almost no evidence of where blood vessels might run. You can fish the beast out of the water and apply tourniquets to the flippers or the tail, but still the unco-operative veins and arteries refuse to reveal themselves. They lie beneath a tight, inflexible layer of blubber, each artery completely surrounded by a cluster of veins. Find the areas where the blubber is thinned and you find a cluster of blood vessels, the vets at Point Mugu told me. Easier said than done. Slight skin discoloration, a depression here and there, the glint of a shallow groove if the moistened tail is held to reflect the light; by such things I would be guided. Then a short needle could be placed in a vessel and a sample of venous, arterial or frequently a mixture of the two bloods taken.

My first essay in blood sampling was right on target. I struck oil. "It doesn't matter much," said Dr. Sam in his relaxed Texan drawl, "if your needle takes blood from vein or artery or a bit of both if you're doin' routine analysis and such, except of course oxygen levels, but don't forget the layout in these critters if you ever want to do an intravenous injection. It's easy as hell to get some of the drug into an artery, it lyin' so close to the veins an' all. So watch out, buddy."

I saw the point. A drug inadvertently injected into an artery instead of a vein will damage the delicate arterial lining, stopping the circulation to tissues supplied by the artery beyond the injection site and causing them to die. At least in land mammals the tough-walled, pulsating arteries are usually easily located and are rarely close to the veins in places where the veterinarian roams in search of injection sites. Already these mermen were leading me, as they were said to lead ancient Greek seafarers, into a new life.

8

Dolphin Handling

From Point Mugu I visited other marine-mammal vets and all the major marinelands in the United States before turning my attention to the dolphin-catching side of the business. Just as a zoo vet must understand the housing, handling and transport of his charges if he is to deal competently with their health problems, so it seemed to me best in this aquatic arena to try to find a water-borne equivalent to head keeper Matt Kelly from whom I could learn the nitty-gritty of the non-veterinary side of dolphins. I found him one March day in Fort Myers, Florida. He made his living catching dolphins in the Gulf of Mexico, his name was Gene Hamilton and with him I had some of the most exciting days of my life.

Like Alice I decided to begin at the beginning and asked Gene if he would take me out with him. A tall, lantern-jawed individual with a taciturn but kindly nature, he agreed, provided that I did exactly what I was told. His catching boat, with low sides and a cutaway stern for pulling animals on deck, could touch sixty miles an hour skimming over the shallow Florida waters, and it could turn on a sixpence at almost full speed. It was no place for novices who got in the way when the hunt was on.

The first thing I learned about catching is that wind is one's prime enemy and patience the greatest virtue. Even a slight breeze, which was welcomed by the yachtsmen and sweating sunbathers of Fort Myers, was enough to put a chop on the water that extended to the horizon. Under such conditions every triangular wavelet could be a dolphin's dorsal fin. The ocean seemed filled with dolphins or, looking at it another way, totally devoid of them. After an overnight storm, the water would be opaque, full of stirred-up sand, and the spotter plane which worked with us as our airborne pointer could not see the groups of dolphins hunting fish shoals under water. So if there was wind or had been wind, and that was most of the time, we sat cutting fish on the rickety old jetty where Gene moored up and put a fortune into the pockets of Mr. Schlitz, brewing beer far away in Milwaukee.

When we did have a calm and glassy sea we would be off early, sometimes before sun-up, to the shallows where the waking dolphins might be collecting a breakfast of mullet, blue runner or butterfish. As the sun climbs out of the grey water we hear the crackle of our spotter plane's radio. In the first good light of the day he has located a group of twelve dolphins feeding quietly ten miles to our north. The pilot, experienced at estimating size and age from a height of several hundred feet, tells us how many animals of the right length, not too young and not too old, not pregnant and not suckling babies, are there for the taking—if we have luck.

We make for the area while Gene's two assistants, bronzed teenagers in frayed jeans shorts, check the catching gear. This is a mile of lightweight, fourteen-foot-deep net which has been carefully folded into zigzag layers and sleeved onto a long bamboo pole which projects over the stern. The top edge of the net is attached to a series of floats and the end nearest the water carries a small sea anchor. The sea anchor is watched carefully. If it were to fall into the ocean before the appointed moment, one mile of net would be unfolded in seconds and it would take an hour or more to retrieve it, sort it out and reposition it along the bamboo pole. While we sail for the catching zone I stand at the wheel talking to Gene, taking lungfuls of cold, morning sea air and munching my share of a bizarre but delicious breakfast of fresh clams, fried frogs' legs and doughnuts, washed down even at that hour with cans of foaming Schlitz.

Before long we hear the buzz of the spotter aircraft somewhere overhead, and the pilot tells us the latest position of our quarry. Cutting the engine speed down to avoid alarming the feeding dolphins, Gene takes the boat towards the school of animals while the spotter keeps up a continual commentary. Suddenly I catch the first thrilling glimpse of a low, dark-grey dorsal fin breaking the water surface for a second as its owner takes in a gulp of air. Then we see another and another. Gene at this point relies almost completely on the aircraft. The pilot, seeing the dolphins' reaction to our approach, for their sensitive ears would have picked up our engine noise miles away, gives instructions that put us in a favourable position for our sweep. To us at almost water level the directions do not seem to make sense, but the pilot is looking down on the chessboard from on high and has a perfect view of all the players in the game. With luck, the dolphins will assume we are just another of the many pleasure boats in Florida's teeming waters. Nevertheless, some of the cowboys who sail such craft are known to indulge in the "sport" of using dolphins for rifle practice. It has made many old bulls wary of any sort of vessel, and the bullet scars that some of them bear are the reason why.

Today all goes according to plan for once, and the spotter plane tells us we are in an ideal position, with the dolphins quietly browsing a hundred yards to our right at two o'clock. He then leaves the scene, and the hunt from now on is conducted solely by Gene. His first action is to tell me, "Sit squarely down on the deck, grab hold of something firm and hold on!" Then he opens the throttle to the full, and the boat leaps forward with a deafening roar and with a punch that leaves the thrill of a ride on Belle Vue's roller coaster in the novice class.

Over the sparkling skin of the water we charge, the boat heeling over as Gene cuts a trench of frenzied foam that arcs across the path of the leading dolphin. The g-forces play musical chairs with my innards and I cling on for dear life, certain that at any moment I will be catapulted through the air like a human cannonball to join the dolphins. The boat stays flat out and the arc continues into a full circle. Gene takes us completely round the school of dolphins and keeps the wheel locked over for a second circuit. Peeping tensely over the gunwales, I can see the animals bobbing and blowing puffs of rainbow-shot vapour in the centre of a broad ring of white water. Gene's aim is to confuse the dolphins by encircling them with a continuous wall of sound from the powerful engines. We have encountered one or two wiser, pluckier leaders of schools (not always bulls, sometimes redoubtable matriarchs) who have made a high-speed beeline run for it, leading their weaker brethren straight through the noise wall and away safely into quiet water, but today the animals are hesitating and milling in the water, uncertain of the best plan of action. Gene observes their indecisive movements, tightens his circular run still further and then roars to his boys, "Shoot!"

At his command one of the boys throws the sea anchor overboard. Gene continues to carve out yet another circle, and all the while the mile of net is being dragged off the bamboo pole like an express train. Round we go, leaving the net floats bobbing in a great curve in our wake until, having completed the full 360 degrees, we come back again to the sea anchor and first float. Gene kills the engines and peers anxiously towards the now fully cast ring of netting, one mile in circumference. There has been no last-minute dash by his quarry, he has not misjudged the water depth, and the nets are deep enough to stop escapers diving underneath; in the centre of the circle a cluster of dark-grey dorsal fins swirl about.

At this stage in the proceedings I was able to stand up again and start to be useful. The first thing was to scan the line of net floats. Evenly spaced, they should all be visible on the water surface. If one or two were submerged it might well mean that the net at that point was being dragged down by some heavy object—like a dolphin enmeshed several feet below and in imminent danger of drowning. "In y'go, Dr. Taylor," Gene would say if we saw such warning signs, and with goggles and a short snorkel tube I would drop over the side into the cool, dark water and make for the spot where the floats had disappeared. Once there I would make an awkward duck dive and pull myself down to where a grey shape might be struggling to free itself from the net. As I glided down I would sometimes hear through the water the alarmed, high-pitched communication squeak of the trapped dolphin. If the animal was not too severely entangled I might free it by hand; otherwise Gene's treasured net had to be cut with a diver's knife. .

Trapped dolphins were not the only cause of the net floats sinking. My first experience of other accidental catches came one sunny afternoon off Key Largo when Gene dropped his nets in a perfect "set" round six or seven immature adult dolphins. The line of floats dipped at two points and, while one of Gene's boys dived to investigate one, I went down to look at the other. Kicking myself under, I followed the net down to where the expected grey form thrashed furiously twelve feet under the surface. Through the fuzzy shadows I could tell that the beast was caught by its head in a hole in the net. It should not be too difficult to pull it back by hand and release it so that it could surface for a welcome gulp of air. Coming closer, I saw to my horror that I was within inches of a seven-foot shark that was lashing its tail to and fro and gnashing its rows of razor-like teeth. I identified it as a black-tipped shark, a species strongly suspected of attacking humans. Should I release it? What would Gene do? Would it attack me if I freed it? Looking at it

9

held in the net by its pectoral fins, I decided to risk a few cuts with my knife before going up again for air. Surely it would be too relieved at its near squeak to try tangling with me. I reached for the knife in my belt and then I saw the second black-tipped shark. Bigger than its companion, it was weaving figures of eight two yards to my left and below me. That made my mind up. In a flurry of bubbles I kicked for the surface and pulled myself thankfully up onto the boat.

"Don't ever fool around with those guys," Gene said when I had told him my story. "If he ain't dead when we pull the nets in, I'll kill him. Hate those guys. Sometimes get a hammerhead or two in with the dolphins messin' up the nets. Ain't no good for anythin' 'cept bait."

"What are blacktips like around here?" I asked.

"Cain't trust 'em," he replied. "Know a dolphin catcher up near Steinhatchee lost a couple o' pounds o' thigh muscle from a blacktip. The doctors who stitched him up knew it was a blacktip by the pattern o' the tooth marks."

That was not the last time I went down to entangled sharks, but whenever I found one I came up fast and left it for Gene to deal with later. I often watched one or another of Gene's boys make similar hurried exits from the water while he laughed and shouted, "Sharks down there? Well, get on your Jesus shoes and walk on the water, fella!"

After clearing the nets of trapped animals, Gene would supervise the slow and meticulous pulling in. The area of the circle was decreased gradually to stop the dolphins panicking and entangling themselves en masse. Little by little the group of captured animals was brought closer to the boat until finally, with one or two men in the water to help, they could be hauled up onto the stern decking. Unsuitable animals were released while those that were to be kept were placed on foam mattresses amidships. There, while the other men pulled in all the net, I had my first experience in handling one hundred per cent wild, dripping

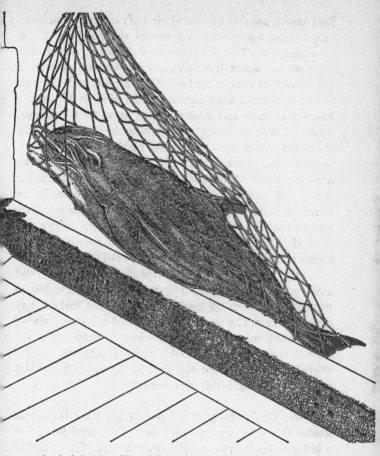

wet, fresh dolphins. The older animals usually lay resignedly, chirping plaintively to one another but not objecting to my touching their bodies. I got, and still get, a sheer physical thrill from contact with the flesh of animals that a few minutes before had been masters of a virtually limitless three-dimensional world where man is a feeble, groping amateur.

When the net was finally aboard and Gene started the engines ready for a fast cruise back to the holding pens at

Fort Myers, another unwanted kind of captive often caused us problems and pain as we tended the dolphins. These were stingrays. This flat relative of the shark, which flies through the water like some marine bat and carries a poisonous flick knife at the base of its whip-like tail, abounds in Florida waters. Very often a number of these fish, even a hundred or more and some weighing up to twelve pounds, would be pulled in along with the dolphin haul. We would throw them back into the sea after picking them out of the net, but some of the slippery, plate-like creatures would fall onto the deck and flip about, unsheathing their poisonous spines and making it perilous underfoot. Occasionally we were inundated with the stingrays, and dead ones would lie all over the boat as we made for home, but even up to many days after its death the poison spines of the fish remain highly active. Once we had the net in, I put on rubber boots to cut the risk of being stung, but the spine of a big ray could easily go through the rubber covering my leg and would go through jeans with no trouble. Gene did not make it any easier for himself by working at all times barefooted, relying on his nimbleness and quick reactions to keep out of the way of the spines that would click up into the armed, offensive position in the twinkling of an eye if a ray was touched or even if it just felt ornery.

It was Gene who gave me one of my most important lessons about the extraordinary ways of the dolphin. It was a bitter but salutary experience; at the end of it a dolphin was dead and I had killed it.

We had caught a young dolphin which was on the point of weaning. It had been captured along with its mother, and both were destined for a famous marineland in California. The youngster struggled and fought when brought aboard and, most significantly, stopped breathing.

"Right now," commanded Gene, "listen good. Young critters like this one will commit suicide by holdin' their breath if you don't watch carefully. Once they're out of the water you gotta time their breathin'. If they go for a maximum, a maximum of two minutes without breathin', we put 'em over the side in a turn or two of net as a sling and let 'em be in the water again. Then they breathe."

"And what then?" I asked.

"Then we pull 'em on board again after a short while and try 'em some more. If they do it again, we dunk 'em again and so on. Usually by the time we get back to Fort Myers and put 'em in the holdin' pens they're OK." Gene wagged a leathery, sun-blackened finger at me. "Now your job, Dr. Taylor, while I get us home lickety-split, is to do nuthin' but watch that little feller and your wrist watch. If he goes more'n two minutes, give a holler and we'll stop and dunk him."

We set off and I sat close to the agitated baby, timing its respiration and pouring sea water over it from time to time to keep the skin from cracking and the body temperature from rising too high. Two minutes went by without the little blowhole opening to suck and blow.

"Whoa!" I yelled, and Gene slowed the engines and came back to help me sling the dolphin and immerse it in the sea. Hanging over the side I watched the youngster breathe normally once it felt the ocean around it. Gene told me that he never had this trouble with bigger specimens.

After two or three minutes we pulled junior back aboard and continued on our way. He took one good breath when he was settled on his pad again, and I noted the time. Two minutes passed with no further breathing. I stopped the boat a second time and we repeated the ducking. Once more the young animal went back to a normal respiration rate of four per minute. Back in the boat again he took a breath and Gene returned to the wheel.

I stared at my watch, following the movement of the second hand, and reflected silently as I squatted by my charge. The breeze streamed through my hair and the sun scorched my naked back. Suicide, Gene had said. Could any animal commit suicide? The mystery of the mass self-drowning of lemmings was a different matter. Could an individual animal just stop breathing and die? Some canonized Catholic virgin was supposed to have taken her life in this way, but normally in mammals the brain simply forces its owner to breathe when the body senses a deficiency of oxygen and an increase of carbon dioxide in the blood. Will power, design, psychological state do not come into it, and shock is a separate thing that produces collapse of the circulation and unconsciousness before death. This little dolphin, though obviously agitated, was conscious and alert and, as far as I could tell from its colour and pulse, its circulation was good.

The seconds ticked by. One minute fifty. I sat on. I knew dolphins' brains ignored high levels of carbon dioxide in the blood when they were diving, but they needed oxygen, demanded it, in the end. That is why eventually they have to surface for air. That is why they drown if trapped in nets. So some involuntary mechanism must make this dolphin breathe and soon.

One minute fifty-nine. I wondered why Gene had said "Two minutes." Surely this was just a good estimate—no, more likely it was a dolphin catcher's unscientific bit of mythology. I watched the second hand pass the two-minute mark and decided to let it carry on without calling Gene yet again. As the watch ticked out the third minute, I knew that orthodox, reliable physiology would prove Gene wrong. It was the unbreakable rules of oxygen deficiency versus the crude rule of thumb of the dolphin catcher.

Four minutes. Still no breath taken by the dolphin. I began to sweat slightly and bite the tip of my tongue. Gene was busy navigating through the shoals. He probably did not know whether two minutes or twelve had gone by. Four and a half minutes. I felt my heart pounding but still trusted the laws of physiology which are common to all mammals from tiny vole to giant elephant. An arrogant voice still whispered, "Oxygen demand must prevail." Four minutes forty-five. The baby dolphin became as still as a plastic model and the pulse faded. My idiot resolve broke and I yelled to Gene, "He's stopped breathing!" The boat came to a stop again and Gene came back to help me lower the dolphin into the water, but it was obvious that this poor creature would never breathe again. It was limp. The eyes were glazing. I had murdered it.

In deep misery I told Gene what I had done. He grimaced but said nothing. Then, as he knelt by the gunwale to release the corpse from the net and let it fall away into the gloomy depths where the sharks patrolled, his knee touched a stingray that had been dead for some time. The erect spine pierced his leg and the barbed point delivered its poison into the vein. White and sweating with pain, he had to endure the worse agony of me withdrawing the spine against the direction of the barbs. Using one of the rubber tubes of my stethoscope as a tourniquet, I bandaged the wound, but within minutes the pain worsened and Gene became very ill. The tough dolphin man stood the wracking agony without uttering one sound, and I made him comfortable on a foam pad while one of his boys took us the rest of the way in. Gene was in bed for nearly a week after that. Dolphin catching was off and all I had to do was to sit on the old jetty, throwing bits of stick into the water and staring miserably out over the dark green expanses of the holding pools, where a big female dolphin dipped and rose without her young son by her sleek side.

When the newly caught dolphins destined for Europe were fully acclimatized and feeding well in the holding pools, they were judged fit to make the long journey over the Atlantic. I had much to learn about this important aspect of dolphin management, too, and the best way to learn was to go with the animals from start to finish, from the sunny coast of Florida to New York and then on to London, Scarborough, Cleethorpes, Nice, Hamburg, Antwerp or Stockholm. Everyone thinks that accompanying dolphins by air from Florida to Europe must be an ideal way of earning one's living. It is not. It is hard, boring, wet, smelly work and it can last for two or three days, particularly if, as happened this time, the first leg of the journey from Miami International to JFK New York is delayed and a missed connection means a twenty-four-hour lie-over in the Big Apple. You cannot take a pair of dolphins along to the nearest Holiday Inn and stick them in your bathroom. If they stay in a cold and windy warehouse in mid-January, you stay too—night and day.

First comes the road journey to Miami with the animals smothered in vaseline or lanolin which gets on your clothes and makes everything tacky. At the airport are the loading and paperwork formalities. I was to find that experienced dolphin handlers avoid excess weight charges by emptying all the water from the crates and removing the recirculating spray pumps and their twelve-volt batteries just before checking in at the freight warehouse. The animal and crate are then weighed and the weight entered on the papers. Now everything can be loaded. On the way to the aircraft, the handler nips quickly round the corner, turns on a tap, runs tens of gallons of water into the crate and replaces the spray equipment and batteries. The dolphins then go onto the plane with the whole load weighing several hundred pounds more than the amount accounted for on the waybill. The alternative, I was told, is to carry water at a cost of five dollars a gallon for the trip. Another source of free water is the washroom on board the cargo planes. The trouble is that if this is overdone the crew of the aircraft complain later that they found no water on board for their needs during the flight and there might be inquiries made.

Batteries for the pumps have a nasty habit of failing at some crucial point along the way. If you are prepared to go completely without sleep in the uncomfortable cargo hold, the constant squirting of water through a large rose spray helps to solve this difficulty. The equally tiresome alternative is to try to buy eight twelve-volt car batteries in the middle of the night somewhere near Kennedy Airport. At that time of day, if you can find a handy garage that is open, the disbelieving guy on duty is likely to demand a fistful of dollars and to regard an American Express card with the enthusiasm he reserves for four-dollar bills.

The endless flight to Europe in what resembles the inside of a giant cigar tube has none of the amusements enjoyed by travellers on passenger flights. Damp and grease go through to your skin. There is the perpetual chore of un-clogging the holes in the spray system which become choked with circulated dolphin droppings, and on bumpy flights the shifting positions of the dolphins in their crates means constant vigilance and a handy supply of cotton-wool pads in case of wounds, eye damage or bedsores. Meanwhile the crew sit forward in their snug cockpit and once in a while pass back a liverwurst sandwich or a beaker of Seven Up as you shiver in your duffle coat and try to find a comfortable squatting position for a minute or two on the treacherous ball-bearings which stud the floor of the cargo hold.

Probably the worst part of the whole journey will be the arrival at London Heathrow. It is not uncommon for a dolphin to wait in the bonded warehouse there for a couple of hours while the customs men take their time about sorting through the mass of paperwork. Rarely will they agree to let the long-suffering beast get on its way while you stay behind to sign all the necessary documents and answer any questions. It is not as if they ever inspect the animals thoroughly for diamonds or contraband hooch, even though it would be quite possible to slip small packages into a dolphin's stomach and the animal would tolerate them for months. No, however much suffering it causes the animals, the customs men work by the book and the dolphins must do likewise.

My first experience of the Heathrow customs was when I went there to receive a giant Pacific octopus from Seattle that arrived, all fifty angry red pounds of him, neatly packed in water, ice and oxygen. This finest of all octopuses is extremely difficult to transport because it tends to pollute the water in which it travels and eventually poisons itself with nitrates produced by its own excrement. Anxious to resuscitate my giant octopus and to give it the chauffeur-driven limousine treatment at express speed all the way to the Yorkshire zoo that had bought it, I had gone out of my way to co-operate with customs.

"There's nothing in my book of duty rates concerning giant octopus," said the official sternly as the minutes ticked by, "but I can't let it go without classifying it. I've got to fill in the right tariff."

"It's a mollusc," I insisted, "like oysters, snails and so on."

The official glowered at the massive, scarlet, tentacled creature in its plastic bag and insulated box. "You mean it's edible?" he queried.

"Well, no, but to make it easier you can classify it as an oyster if you like."

"Oysters are on my list, but he doesn't look anything like an oyster, or a snail."

"Don't you eat little squid, calamares, in Spain or Italy ever?" I asked. The octopus was getting madder and redder and passing more droppings. I had to get it out of there and away with new water and oxygen.

"Nope," said the customs man, "don't like nasty foreign food. Squid? Yuk!"

"Please, please," I said, "take my word for it. It's the same family as oysters. Look that lot up in your tariff book and charge me at the same rate."

At last commonsense prevailed. My octopus was entered on the import documents as "One unusually large shell-less whelk". The customs man had had the last word, and what did it matter to me if he considered this scarlet kraken a variety of the humble whelk which is so good with vinegar, salt and pepper? At least I had got away.

As a direct result of this experience, when I returned with the Florida dolphins I did my first and only bit of animal smuggling. I was bringing back an unusual present for Belle Vue's aquarium in the shape of a bunch of horseshoe crabs, primitive, helmet-shaped creatures that abound in the canals and round the shores of Florida. I put a dozen adults, each ten inches across, in the water beneath a dolphin slung in its crate. Coming to count the single "fish", the customs officer noticed the spiky, rod-like tails of the large crabs projecting above the water surface as the creatures shuffled about below.

"Whassat?" asked the official.

"Horseshoe crabs," I replied.

"Crabs? What for?"

Oh dear, I thought, not again. I bet my bottom dollar that this unique descendant of the trilobites, a group whose other representatives became extinct two hundred million years ago, would not be in the tariff book.

"Er, the crabs are for the dolphins. Animal food for en route," I lied.

"Oh, fine. Of course," said the customs man. "I suppose they've got to have a nibble on the way like us." The crabs and I had won through.

Arrived at their destination, the dolphins were lowered into a shallow pool, their first feel of salt water in days. Even then, my work was not done. Stiff and sore from the journey, the animals had difficulty balancing themselves in the water. This went on for a further eight hours, but until they were able to swim freely and safely, I had to go in with them. Though dog tired, I would walk them round and round their pool, guiding them by holding onto their dorsal fins. No, dolphin transporting is not much fun.

One of the dolphins I brought back from the Gulf of

Mexico was destined for the London Dolphinarium on Oxford Street, a place where dolphins, sea lions, penguins and beautiful girls put on non-stop shows in a converted theatre. There were marvellous sound and lighting effects, and professional actors presented the shows. Behind the scenes, beneath Soho Square, there were holding pools and facilities where I crammed in among leggy chorus girls and kept the dolphin stars up to scratch under intensely artificial conditions. It was a good training ground for me in working against the odds in show business, preparing for the days when I would go to Paris to examine dolphins in the glass pool at the famous Moulin Rouge, the only dolphinarium where the management has ever informed me that "When 'e 'as finished, ze veterinarian can take a shower weez ze girls eef 'e wishes, like ze French vet used to do."

Unfortunately, although brilliantly conceived, the London Dolphinarium was built in the shopping area of the West End where passers-by were more likely to seek coffee shops· than wander into Flipper shows in their breaks between bouts of buying and window gazing. The Dolphinarium was eventually forced to close, but before it did I had driven down from the north at least once a week to sort out one problem or another with the animal and occasionally with the human performers. When the dolphins started roughing up some of the girl "aquamaids" swimming with them in the water, I was called in to help. The girls were getting bruised and alarmed by the dolphins' boisterous attentions, the shows suffered and some of the ladies talked of resigning. I found that the animals were detecting minute quantities of pheromones, sex chemicals, in the water during the days that the girls had their monthly periods. The attacks turned out in fact to be vigorous amorous advances, triggered off by the chemicals. Once the dolphin roués had been given shots of a drug normally used to turn the minds of human sex criminals to higher things, peace and good shows returned to the Dolphinarium.

One day, Clyde, the dolphin at the London Dolphinarium whom I had accompanied across the Atlantic, fell severely ill with liver inflammation. I struggled with the case, sleeping for a couple of nights beside the pool on a makeshift bed of an upturned rubber dinghy, and gradually Clyde began to pull round. He would need a massive dose of vitamin B complex by intravenous injection, so he was taken from the water and laid carefully on a thick mat of plastic foam. With two men holding the dolphin firmly, I slowly pressed a new, fine needle into the tail. A dark gout of blood welled up. Vein. I improved the flow by edging down a fraction more and stared intently at the blood. It was blackish, surely all of it de-oxygenated blood from a vein. Then I noticed the finest hair-thin wisp of pillar-box red. I recalled Dr. Sam's "Watch out, buddy" at Point Mugu. Probably the needle was drawing from veins and from the central artery. I pulled the needle back a whisker. Now all seemed blackish blood again. I must be in a vein and a vein alone. Trying not to alter the needle's position, I carefully connected the loaded syringe, sucked back to check all was well and then gently depressed the plunger. The vitamin B went into Clyde's circulation, he was returned to the pool apparently unperturbed and continued to make a fine recovery over the next forty-eight hours. We were all delighted.

Then, three days after the intravenous shot, I received a worrying phone call. A strange mark had appeared on Clyde's tail, a pale streak that was long and showed smaller branches, rather like a fern. Clyde was showing signs of pain and irritation in the area, an area as important to the motive power of the dolphin as a propeller is to an ocean liner. I went to look. Sure enough, the fern-like mark was distinct but only on one half of the tail, the half where I had given my shot, and it began at exactly the point where I had introduced my needle. For the first time in my life I had given at least part of an injection by mistake into an artery. Glumly I knew that the vitamin B, an irritant chemical, had gone whipping along the artery and into its tributaries. Thrombosis had occurred, the tissues supplied by the artery beyond my injection had died and I could expect them to drop off. It was a classic case of iatrogenic gangrene or, in honest layman's terminology, a real screw-up by the vet. There was little I could do. Dead tissue is dead tissue. I could encourage it to slough off, prevent secondary infection and wait. The nub of the question was how much tissue did that artery supply and so how much had died? If half the tail dropped off eventually, how would Clyde swim? I lay awake during those nightmare hours between two o'clock and five o'clock in the morning when only ill humours are abroad and sweated as I imagined the prospects.

As the days passed the pale, fern-like area became an ugly yellow colour, expanded and began to soften. At last after a week it was clear that I could see all the dead area; it had stopped expanding and the rotting tissue was beginning to peel away. A broad band ran down the centre of one tail fluke, but to my relief it seemed very unlikely that half the tail was going to fall off since the rest of the fluke looked healthy and was apparently well furnished with blood. What had seemed to be the main vessel supplying the tail fluke must have been backed up by other, smaller arteries which were not its tributaries and had been undamaged. Dolphins were obviously designed marvellously in yet another respect, to keep erring veterinarians from screwing up their engines.

After many anxious days, Clyde's tail eventually cast off all the dead tissue, leaving a deep wide trench which had gone right down to the fibrous core of the fluke. Still, the tail worked. Clyde jumped, somersaulted and spun. My job was to get this gaping hole filled as quickly as possible. Twice a day I arranged for it to be coated with a healing cream and then thickly plastered with Grandmother's water-resistant denture fixative. After a month Clyde had completely healed and I could sleep dreamlessly again, but a long, fronded snow-white scar remains to this day to remind me whenever I see him that "mainlining" a dolphin is one of the most hazardous of procedures.

9

The Burning Bear
and Other Crises

After the exciting days at Point Mugu and on Gene's boat off the coast of Florida, I began to consider seriously what had always been just a dream: setting up a practice to treat nothing but exotic species. It would be some time yet, though, before my zoo experience and contacts would be wide enough to take such a big step into the unknown, and until then it was back to cows and sheep on moorland farms and cats and dogs in the Rochdale surgery. For exotic animal work I would continue to rely mainly on surgery cases and on Belle Vue Zoo.

It was from there that Ray Legge telephoned me one autumn evening. "I've got a bear on fire! Get here sharp as you can!" I hardly had time to pick up the phone and put the receiver to my ear before Ray's unusually strident voice rapped out the message. Before I could ask any details, there was a click. He had rung off.

When Ray's abrupt call came in I was just putting the final touches to my favourite dish of hare, Lièvre à la Royale, an exquisite casserole containing cream, cognac and pine kernels. From the dressing of the shot wild hare after it had hung a week, something Shelagh insisted I do alone in the farthest corner of the garden, through the marinading in wine and herbs and the blending of the chopped liver and heart with the brandy, a relaxing and enjoyable culinary exercise with which I insisted Shelagh should not interfere, the whole process took twenty-four hours. Now at last, with its accompanying wafers of glazed carrots and rosemary-sprinkled potatoes, it was almost ready for the table. But the burning bear banished all thoughts of dinner.

"Don't worry, love," said Shelagh, as I whipped off my blue-and-white-striped cooking apron and picked up my emergency bag, "it'll warm up tomorrow." She pushed a couple of apples into my duffle coat pocket.

As I wound my way laboriously through the evening traffic towards the zoo I puzzled over Ray's call. He had sounded worried all right, but more than that I had the impression that he was mightily angry. I had never seen Ray, the epitome of the well-mannered English gentleman, blazing with rage the way he had sounded on the phone. A burning bear? It sounded like vandals. We have more than our fair share of those in a city zoo. Yes, vandals must have done something particularly obnoxious to raise his wrath. A burning bear sounded just that.

When I arrived in the zoo grounds my headlights illuminated a cluster of men standing near the bear pit. One of the group was in a state of great agitation, almost literally jumping up and down and stamping round in small circles. It was Ray Legge. The other figures I recognized as members of the Board of Directors. I stopped the car and walked over to join them.

"And if it happens once more, just once more, I'll walk out of this place and, by God, I'll . . ." Ray was white with anger. The Board members were listening silently; some looked crestfallen, others embarrassed. "Just look at that animal, will you?" Ray was in full spate. "You can't have it both ways, you won't have it both ways! It's my animals or your Battle of Waterloo. Your damned Battle of Waterloo will have to go!"

In the bear pit a brown bear sat on a rock licking at a frizzled black patch as big as a saucer on its side. On the ground nearby lay a large burnt-out rocket, a firework with a stick at least four feet long. From its charred casing a plume of grey smoke curled lazily upwards. I understood. Damned Battle of Waterloo! Every autumn Belle Vue presented for two or three weeks a lavish evening firework display. Combined with son et lumière and several dozen men in period costume, historic battles would be re-enacted in a deafening, dazzling pyrotechnic spectacular. Last year it had been General Wolfe storming the heights of Quebec. This year it was Waterloo. The problem was that the hour-long barrage of star shells, firecrackers and smoke bombs was all staged in an arena backing directly onto the bear pits where the collection of Himalayan, brown, sun, polar and sloth bears ate, slept, went about their quiet daily business and, most importantly, mated. They were literally only inches away from the crackling rockets and roaring catherine wheels.

Both Ray and I had been complaining bitterly about the effects on the animals of being compulsorily in the orchestra pit during every performance of the ear-splitting extravaganza. We were particularly concerned for the polar bears and their efforts to produce young: we were certain that each year our lovely adult female conceived and, if things had progressed as nature intended, she would have delivered one or maybe two little cubs in November or December. It never happened. On came the fireworks at the end of September, and within a few days the keeper cleaning out the dens would find a smear of blood or perhaps remains which proved conclusively that the bear had once again miscarried and devoured the half-grown embryo. It was heartbreaking, but now this!

Ray broke off his tirade and came over to me. "That bear felt like sleeping outside on the rocks tonight. The keeper couldn't get him into the sleeping quarters." If a bear feels like napping al fresco on a mild night, there is no easy way of changing his mind. "Then that bloody pantomime started up, a rocket went off course and landed in the pits." He was quivering with fury. "Do you know, when the keeper called me the bear was actually alight! Fur in flames!" He spat out the words with slow, precise venom. "I've told them. That's the last straw. The fireworks must go because we can't move the bears."

I darted the bear with a tranquillizing syringe and climbed down a ladder into the pit. The burnt area of the skin had been largely insulated by the dense, sizzling hair but it was still a serious and painful injury. I plastered it liberally with a paste containing local anaesthetic, antibiotic and cortisone. It would heal all right. Climbing back out of the pit, I found Ray still expostulating and gesticulating with the directors.

To our amazement, his war dance did produce all that we could have hoped for. The stray rocket turned out in the end to be a twenty-four-carat blessing in disguise, for it was decided that the annual fireworks displays at Belle Vue should end. Ray and I were delighted. Now maybe we would get our first baby polar bear.

The key to successful breeding of this species in captivity appears to be ultra-quiet privacy for the female. We decided that from October onwards next year, Crystal, Belle Vue's female polar bear, would be placed in strict isolation in a secluded, dark den, with food placed silently from time to time in an adjoining compartment which she could reach through a small door. No mucking out, no regular inspections by flashlight—just leave her alone. Then, if all went well, we might hear the soft squeaks of the hidden cubs some time before Christmas and get our first glimpse of them in the following January when she decided to show them to us.

The next breeding season came round, and true to form the female polar bear conceived. We went ahead with our plan and treated her like a hermit. Just after Christmas the keeper heard faint mewing noises in her den. They continued for a day and then ceased. Some days later the bear moved into the feeding compartment and insisted on staying there, clawing at the door that led to the outside pits. We let her out and searched her den. Inside was the shrivelled body of a full-term cub, but without a drop of mother's milk in its tummy.

The following year the same thing happened, but this time she half ate the baby. Ray and I were despondent. "Well," I said, "next season we'll hand-rear the cub right from birth."

"How do you reckon to get the cub away before she eats it or at least does it some harm?"

"As soon as the keeper hears any squeaking or gets any hint at all that she's given birth, you (I'm bound to be at least half an hour away, maybe more, and that could be too long) you will knock her out with phencyclidine and grab the cub. Beginning in mid-October we'll have a dart already loaded with the right dose of phencyclidine standing permanently in a jar outside her den. And we'll start the little 'uns off on Carnation milk."

Ray nodded. All we had to do now was to wait an interminable ten or eleven months to see if our plan would work.

Ironically, in view of my hard-won connection with the zoo and the amount of time I spent there, Belle Vue could not help very much with my increasing interest in learning about marine mammals. The only ones in the zoo were three big old Californian sea lions that lived in the wooden Victorian pavilion, jealously guarded by their trainer, an elderly German lady called Mrs. Schmidt. Mrs. Schmidt had a lifetime's experience in working with sea lions. She worried and doted and fussed over the honking, snorting, four-hundred-pound monsters, rarely taking a day off and meticulously selecting and preparing all their food herself.

No one, but no one, be he head keeper or zoo director, and certainly not that meddlesome harbinger of death, the veterinarian, got within spitting distance of her beloved Adolf, Heinz and Dieter. Mrs. Schmidt took no chances; she even took her baths in the sea-lion house, sitting in an old tub and bellowing shrill Teutonic oaths if anyone made to approach the door. It was tacitly accepted by everyone that the sea-lion house was Mrs. Schmidt's private preserve. Left alone in her sanctum sanctorum she caused nobody any trouble and asked for nothing but the regular delivery of fish. Even Matt Kelly was a little in awe of her.

There was no salt water in the sea-lion pool, no filtration or chlorination equipment. The sweet water was changed when it became foul. The fish for the animals was fresh from the Lancashire docks and thus did not undergo the deep-freezing that would kill any parasites it contained. As a result of all this, Adolf, Heinz and Dieter were constantly taking in worm eggs by mouth and from time to time would excrete the long, wriggly, clay-coloured adult parasites. This would send Mrs. Schmidt hurrying to the nearby chemist's for extract of santonin, the stuff that she had always used on sea lions, as had her father before her. Santonin extract generally resulted in a pleasing expulsion of a biggish bundle of worms, but in the process the animals would suffer a few hours of griping pain in the guts and would grind their teeth with a most despondent air.

Mrs. Schmidt was used to that. "Those verdammte worms!" she would explain. "They fight to their last gasp to keep a hold. See how they make my three lieblings unhappy while they thrash about and struggle to resist my santonin. Still, all will be well shortly. I always get those verdammte Würmer!" And she would nod contentedly.

Sure enough, the three sea lions would soon recover from the worming and would be rewarded with choice whole whiting—whiting which contained invisible worm eggs and sometimes even invisible baby worm larvae.

If Adolf had a cold, Mrs. Schmidt gave him Fenning's fever powders, cloves of garlic and spoonfuls of honey secreted inside the fish. When Dieter got a boil and would not eat, she smeared the throbbing lump with Germolene and kept him locked in his pen away from the pool in the hope that he would drink from a bowl of water into which she had mixed some mysterious "blood-purifying" salts. In all the years and years that she had been at Belle Vue she had never once taken veterinary advice. I rarely ventured inside her domain and then only to catch the sea lions' show with the paying public. It struck me that the big animals were slow and lethargic considering their high degree of training, but my knowledge of marine mammals was still limited and perhaps it was just their great weight.

There were times when Ray Legge knew that one or another of the sea lions was not up to the mark and he would diplomatically suggest that perhaps Dr. Taylor might be able to help—after all, he was being paid for his veterinary advice—but Mrs. Schmidt would simply retreat within her pavilion, bolt the door and prepare to withstand a siege. If Ray took a firmer line she would just as adamantly but politely refuse the offer, send her assistant to the chemist so that her lines could not be infiltrated while she herself was away, and even sleep at nights by the side of her charges just in case we tried a secret nocturnal examination of the beasts. "You can't be too careful" seemed to be her motto.

The worms in the sea lions came and went and new ones took their place. One day Mrs. Schmidt noticed an unusually large number of live worms lying on the pool bottom. Mein Gott! The three boys had picked up a bigger load of parasites than ever. She decided to take stern measures with the disgusting invaders. It looked as if a particularly numerous band of the pests was involved; ach so! A double dose of the santonin extract would deal with them. Adolf, Heinz and Dieter duly swallowed their medicine hidden inside a whole fish. Half an hour later it appeared to Mrs. Schmidt that the worms were fighting far more ferociously than normal. The sea lions were getting the expected gripes and colly-wobbles, but something she had never seen before was also happening. The animals were beginning to vomit violently, tremble uncontrollably and shake their heads in a bizarre, glassy-eyed fashion. Sudden powerful spasms shook their sleek, chubby bodies. They were in trouble. The worms were winning!

As the minutes passed and the sea lions showed no signs of recovering, Mrs. Schmidt made a momentous decision; she would ask Mr. Legge's advice. Ray went down to the sea-lion house as soon as she appeared white-faced in his office to tell him with much agitation what had happened. It was plain when he saw the distressed trio that something had gone horribly wrong with the worming, and he called me right away.

Adolf and Co. were in fact showing all the symptoms one could expect from an overdose of santonin. Santonin is a poison derived from the dried buds of a plant named wormwood by ancient apothecaries after they had observed its properties. The use of it in the old days relied on the poison bumping off the parasitic worms at a dose which was low enough not to do the same to the worms' host. It is a chemical that attacks the central nervous system, and the signs that the worms were putting up a heroic resistance, as Mrs. Schmidt interpreted them, were in fact the effects of the toxic substance on the sea lions themselves.

Now at last I was presented with my first marine mammal case at Belle Vue. It was a breakthrough, but I could hardly have chosen a more inauspicious debut than three un-restrainable sea-lion bulls with the signs of nerve poisoning produced by a chemical to which there was no antidote.

Although the vomiting and diarrhoea should evacuate any of the santonin that remained unabsorbed by the intestine, the dramatic convulsions continued. I decided to try a tran-quillizer, but it would have to be injected, and sea lions are one of the species on which it is risky to use the dart-gun because of the danger of dirt from the skin being carried into the animal's system by the dart.

Kelly had arrived on the scene and was shaking his broad head pessimistically as he looked at the agonized animals. "Can you and Matt hold them somehow while I give them a shot?" I asked Ray. The sea lions were in a small pen containing a pool from which the water had been drained. They were conscious and obviously aware of our presence. It would be impossible to pin down such heavy creatures and, like most sea mammals, the sea lion is designed without any convenient grab handles.

"I'll get a chair," said Ray. "If you can get a needle into the back flipper muscle somehow, I'll try to distract the head end."

Mrs. Schmidt produced a chair, and the zoo director took up the classical lion tamer's pose with the four wooden legs pointing towards the jerking head of the agonized Heinz. We both knew how dirty sea-lion teeth are and what severe bites they can inflict on one another and on man; Mrs. Schmidt bore gnarled scars on her hands and arms. Protected, I hoped, by Ray and his chair, I splashed some disinfectant onto Heinz's skin and jabbed a new needle into his rump. He was too wracked with the convulsions to do anything more than turn his head slightly in my direction. The tranquillizer slipped into the muscle. Adolf and Dieter were treated in the same way, then we stood and waited while Mrs. Schmidt continued to marvel at the powerful rearguard action by the worms. Slowly the sea lions relaxed, the convulsions diminished and the vomiting ceased. After three quarters of an hour it looked as if the three sea lions were going to be all right. They were drowsy but undoubtedly out of danger.

"Now, Mrs. Schmidt," I said, feeling able to take advantage of the situation, "that's the last time that you will use santonin on *our* sea lions." She blinked and did not say a word. Matt stood by, looking like a sergeant-major quietly enjoying the dressing-down of one of his privates by the CO. "From now on," I continued, "we will use something new. It's very effective and not at all poisonous. I'll send you a bottle of piperazine tablets tomorrow."

Adolf, Heinz and Dieter did fully recover but in a few weeks began to show evidence of worm infestation again. Obediently, Mrs. Schmidt gave them the piperazine tablets. Delightedly she watched the worms expelled a few hours later, and much to her amazement not one single worm put up a struggle. The sea lions had no gripes, no diarrhoea, no grinding of teeth.

Mrs. Schmidt continued to feel, I think, that although I might be Lord of the Worms, the rest of my medical art was still suspect. At least I had penetrated the sea-lion house and was allowed to look at the animals whenever I wanted—unless their keeper was bathing. It was a major advance, but I still had the impression that the sea lions were slow and sluggish in their movements. They seemed to tire easily and they lay around idly; there was none of the zest I had seen in sea lions at other zoos. At the time little of importance had been published about sea-lion medicine, so the special nutritional problems that pinnipeds (seals, sea lions and walruses) and other marine mammals can develop in captivity had not yet been realized.

One day, as I watched Mrs. Schmidt prepare fish pieces for Adolf and his partners, it struck me that for every bucket of fish she filled with choice cuts for her "boys", she was filling another bucket with waste pieces to throw away. She was neatly filleting the fish, removing bones, heads, tails and all the internal organs. The sea lions got only one hundred per cent meat, first-quality steaks. In the wild, sea lions naturally eat the whole fish, bones, guts and all, as well as huge quantities of squid and cuttlefish. I discovered that for years the Belle Vue sea lions had received only the boneless middle cuts of herring, whiting and mackerel.

"What about supplements?" I asked. "Do you give minerals or vitamins?"

"No. Nor have I in all the years I've been keeping sea lions, Doctor," came the reply.

"Right, I'm going to give you some multivitamin syrup," I said. "Put a tablespoonful in their fish each day." She agreed. "And what's more," I added, "I want you to stop filleting the fish. You can remove the guts if you like, but I don't see how these animals can get enough calcium without the bones in their diet."

Mrs. Schmidt looked horrified but she promised to do what I asked. I sent down to her the first multivitamin syrup I laid my hands on in the dispensary, a lemon-flavoured concoction made up for human geriatric patients. Apart from the flavouring it contained nothing but a mixture of the vitamins A, B, C and D.

A few days later I was driving through the zoo grounds when I saw Mrs. Schmidt running towards my car waving her arms to attract my attention. Oh-oh, here's trouble, I said to myself as I wound down the window.

"Dr. Taylor, Dr. Taylor, you must come and see my boys," she said, puffing with the exertion. Apart from her flushed face I was surprised to see that she did not appear alarmed or angry. If anything she was in rather a pleasant mood. Good Lord, Mrs. Schmidt had actually smiled at me!

I went into the sea-lion house. There were Adolf, Heinz and Dieter playing in the pool and gambolling around on the stage. But how they were playing! The three ponderous fellows were no longer torpid or slow-moving. They were sliding, rolling, diving and leaping in the water like young otters.

"It's the vitamins, Doctor," crowed Mrs. Schmidt, "it's the vitamins. I've never seen them so alert and active. I thought they were in peak condition but look how wrong I was."

She was right: it was the vitamins, probably the vitamin B_1 in particular. It is a wonder that those animals survived at all when they were deprived of minerals and the all-important vitamin B_1. Years later we were to discover how essential these substances are to marine mammals fed on dead fish like herring and mackerel, which contain a potent enzyme that utterly destroys vitamin B; and how dangerous the lack of salt could be to specimens kept in fresh water.

The conquest of Mrs. Schmidt and her sea-lion house was complete, but I became increasingly nervous about driving near the pale blue wooden pavilion. She seemed to sense that I was in the grounds and would come flying out with a thousand questions about every minute thing that might or she imagined might be wrong with her boys. As for the lemon-flavoured liquid, she refused ever to change from it. When more suitable, more concentrated tablets with the same constituents were given to her, she swore that they did not work as well as the lemon syrup. And when the drug company making the product changed the flavouring from lemon to orange for some reason, she kicked up a mighty fuss in Ray Legge's office. "Dr. Taylor said I should use the lemon syrup and look what wonders it performed," she thundered. "I must have the *lemon* one!" When it was made absolutely clear that no more lemon was ever going to be produced and that Dr. Taylor had personally checked the credentials of the orange substitute, she gave in. I do not think Mrs. Schmidt ever treated another ailment in her sea lions again, and she made it her business to see that no one, but no one, except myself went anywhere near her precious boys.

Driving back to the surgery one day after I had been to the sea-lion house at Mrs. Schmidt's excited request to see the effect of my vitamins on her threesome, I stopped at some traffic lights. Casually looking at the other vehicles around me, I thought I recognized an individual sitting next to the driver of the car on my immediate right. Bigger and shaggier than when I had first encountered him when he was a baby, he was dressed in corduroy dungarees, purple chunky-knit woollen sweater and Sinatra hat. He was holding one side of an unfolded road map while his human chauffeur held the other and studied their whereabouts. If I was not mistaken it was Billy, a chimpanzee I had once treated for pinworms. He had been owned at the time by a rather overwhelming woman named Mrs. Lomax. I tapped on my window.

Billy glanced superciliously in my direction and then, apparently unable to place my face as belonging to anyone important, and bored stiff by yet another of those oddballs who would insist on gesticulating, waving, winking and generally making asses of themselves every time he did nothing more remarkable than go out for a drive, he yawned histrionically and looked down at the map. I could not quite see Billy's companion at the wheel, and wondered whether it was Mr. Lomax and he was trying to make his way to see me.

I had not been in the surgery for five minutes before Billy and his friend were ushered in. It was indeed Mr. Lomax, a portly, pink-faced man with a high-pitched voice, an ever perspiring brow that required frequent mopping with a large blue-spotted handkerchief, and a tight grey suit the pockets of which bristled with pencils and ballpoints and the seat of which was so polished that I might have expected to see Billy's impish reflection glinting in it. Mr. Lomax wore socks that did not match.

"Dr. Taylor," he piped, "my wife sends her apologies. She couldn't come because she has a speaking engagement in Bradford. I've been sent—I mean, I've brought Billy with his problem."

"Problem? The worms again, you mean?"

Mr. Lomax shook his head vigorously. "Oh no. We, well, he's absolutely OK in that respect these days. What's worrying her, us, is the way his tummy's swelling."

I looked at the now mature ape sitting placidly on the floor holding the neatly folded road map in both hands. He was big, hairy, muscular and very much the macho male chimpanzee. True enough, he did look eight months pregnant. His purple piece of home knit was stretched over a distinct pot belly.

"Can you handle Billy?" I asked, noting the chimp's now well developed fang teeth, which he displayed from time to time as he gave me the apprehensive chimp grin.

"Not really, to be honest. Billy's a mummy's boy. But if you wouldn't mind looking at him on the floor, and if I keep giving him these Smarties"—hesitantly he produced a large bag of iced chocolate drops from a pocket—"you can probably examine him down there."

I certainly did not mind. Not for the first time I would sit on the floor with a patient to avoid starting a potentially disastrous rough-house by trying to get the beast onto the examination table. I am one Mahomet who, for the sake of a peaceful and productive examination, is prepared to go to any mountain anywhere.

"Apart from the swelling has Billy shown any sign of illness?" I inquired.

"He's a bit more peeky than usual, we think. He threw a milk bottle at the next-door neighbour's dog last week—knocked a tooth out and we had to pay the vet's bill—and he's not eating quite as well as usual. Gone off his fried liver and onions and his bedtime Ovaltine. He's still fairly lively though. He got into the bathroom when my sister-in-law was washing her hair, pinched her electric drier and dropped it down the loo. Blew all the fuses. Sister-in-law had to go to a Masonic dinner with a wig on. He's taking his fruit and vegetables fine, though. Droppings? Well, she —my wife—changes his nappies, you know. He did take his clothes off the other night when we were asleep. Nappies and all. Did his business on the piano. No, no sign of diarrhoea or anything. Very normal, I'd say—I know because I cleaned the piano myself."

I sat on the surgery floor near Billy, and Mr. Lomax bent down and started to feed Smarties into the mobile black lips with the frenzy of a slot-machine addict. Cautiously I stroked Billy's head and slyly let my hand caress downwards over one cheek. Billy seemed to like it. He stuck one index finger into my ear. I let it stay there; it was only marginally uncomfortable and seemed a reasonable quid pro quo. As my fingers lay on Billy's cheek I gently pulled down the lower eyelid. He seemed paler than normal. Pretending to flip idly at his lips, I pulled them out a little so that I could inspect the gums; they were not as freshly pink as I would have liked either. Billy kept his finger in my ear and with the other hand tried to push the corner of the road map into my mouth. I pursed my lips and quietly raised my hand to ease away his arm and to indicate that while I might tolerate an earful of finger, a mouthful of paper was out of the question. I also used the opportunity to take his pulse as I held his wrist. It was normal. So far so good. The examination was proceeding well and Billy was still unperturbed. Next I slipped my hand under his sweater. The chimp hooted a warning at me and pulled the finger from my ear, making ready to clout me if I showed any sign of trying to take his clothes off. I cooed at him and tickled his navel as I explored his abdomen beneath the sweater. Billy relaxed, but took a grip of the hem of his sweater just in case.

The swelling of the stomach was undoubtedly more than just obesity or slack abdominal muscles, conditions often seen in young, imperfectly fed great apes, particularly gorillas. A tense, round mass the size of a large grapefruit lay in the body cavity. It did not seem to be painful, and it was possible to move it slightly from place to place within the abdomen.

For ten minutes I carefully explored the contours of the mass and went through the possibilities in my mind. Abscess, cyst, tumour? Amoeba cavity, common in chimps? Tapeworm hydatids? Which organ was involved: liver, spleen, intestines? Or no organ—just an independent mass attached to the peritoneum? I debated whether to take a biopsy sample, but decided that it would only delay the major operation which I felt sure would be necessary. Better perhaps to operate and remove the mass and then confirm its true nature. That would avoid both the need for anaesthetizing twice and the possibility of the biopsy producing side effects like peritonitis; it would also save time if the lump was in any way malignant. On balance I thought that the mass was most likely a non-malignant cyst, lying fairly free in the abdomen or possibly embracing most of the spleen and containing pus produced by the same amoeba parasite that causes dysentery in man. Whatever it was, Billy was going to undergo major surgery.

Mr. Lomax had to have a chair to sit on when I stood up and told him what I had found. "It's not the thought of the operation that upsets me, Dr. Taylor," he squeaked, sponging his pink jowls with his handkerchief. "It's, well, it's the thought of telling her—my wife. She'll have a fit! She'll want to know how he got this trouble—she's sure there's no healthier chimp than Billy."

"I understand," I replied truthfully—I remembered her as a formidable, excitable woman—"but it would be unwise to pretend that there is anything else to be done in the circumstances. No operation and there may well be no Billy before long."

I saw them to the door and watched as they crossed the outer office, Billy carrying the road map in one hand and belabouring Mr. Lomax's backside with the Sinatra hat held in the other.

I had arranged for Billy to be brought to the surgery in four days' time, with an empty stomach and a spoonful of tranquillizing syrup administered in a cup of fruit juice just before setting out. Operation day arrived and promptly at ten o'clock Billy, accompanied now by Mrs. Lomax herself, was brought into my office. She was a stringy, pale, middle-aged lady, with a querulous voice and fidgety manner. To my dismay the chimp showed no signs of having taken any tranquillizer, and I did not fancy jabbing needles into him while he was fully conscious.

"He just would not drink the fruit juice with the drug in it," his owner confessed. "He seemed to know there was something added."

At my request, the normally modish chimp was undressed. He looked mean and hungry. Spotting a small packet of Nescafé powder and a sugar cube lying on my desk ready for my mid-morning brew of coffee, he swept both items into his mouth with one fast "lodger's reach", as Lancastrians call such swift light-fingeredness. After swallowing the goodies, he spat out the indigestible paper. Still mean and still hungry, he looked round the room for something else to eat. Ominously he began cracking his knuckles. Everything else was ready for the operation, but first I somehow had to get some injectable anaesthetic into Billy. He was obviously in no mood to be trifled with and there is no way to restrain a full-grown chimp who does not feel like letting folk prick him with needles. I would have to use the dart-gun and, for the first and only time in my career to date, I prepared to shoot a knock-out syringe at a free-ranging chimpanzee on the prowl in my own surgery waiting room. Loading the gas-pistol with a small syringe charged with a dose of phencyclidine, I explained what I planned to do. "Billy will have to be left on his own in the waiting room."

"No, never!" wailed Mrs. Lomax.

"Yes, definitely. There's no other way and I can't risk having humans about when I start firing darts in a confined space. No one can stay in with Billy. I'll open the door a crack, shoot at him, close the door and then, when he goes to sleep, we'll carry on in the normal way. By the way, Mrs. Lomax, I suggest that you go shopping for a couple of hours after he's knocked out." I did not want her hanging round the premises while I operated.

Vulnerable items like photo frames, potted plants and an electric fire were removed from the waiting room and Billy was slipped in there. Behind the closed door we listened. I had to be certain he was at the other side of the room before I did my bit of sniping. There was a bumping as Billy moved among some of the chairs; then I heard a shuffling noise.

He was rifling through the magazines on the table by the far wall. This was my chance.

I opened the door a few inches, put my foot against the bottom of it and held firmly onto the door handle, ready to close it should Billy try joining us. With one eye at the crack I glimpsed a crouching Billy looking at me from a distance of three yards. I took aim with my gun hand and squeezed the trigger. Plop! From the angry screeching I knew that the dart had struck chimp flesh. Before I could close the door, Billy had snatched the missile out of his buttocks, where it had lodged and discharged its contents in a fraction of a second, and flung it accurately back at me. Not for the first time I nearly took a returned dart full in the face. Great apes often return my ammunition in this way, which is helpful of them I suppose, but I shudder to think what would happen if I was hit by one which had not fired its drug load. There is no antidote to a big dose of phencyclidine, and I can just see the headline in the *Rochdale Observer*: "Veterinarian put to sleep by chimpanzee." A different way to go.

The dart whipped through the still partly opened door and embedded itself firmly in the corridor wall. With a crash I shut the door just before Billy hurled himself at the other side. Hollering with annoyance, he pounded the door and threatened to split the panelling. Then he wreaked his fury on our chairs. There were tearing and shredding noises, too, as copies of *The Field* and *Illustrated London News* were turned into ticker tape. Gradually the echoes of bedlam subsided and all was still. Six minutes had passed since the darting. Billy should now be chasing lady chimpanzees in a sunlit happy valley, for we know that small doses of phencyclidine in humans tend to produce fanciful erotic dreams. I opened the door. Sure enough, Billy lay sprawled and sleeping on a heap of chairs and pieces of chair.

With Mrs. Lomax sent fretfully packing, the chimpanzee was carried into the operating room and I deepened his anaesthesia with oxygen and halothane gas. Scrubbed and gowned, and with the patient shaved and painted a startling antiseptic red over his bulging belly, I took a scalpel and unzipped his abdomen from top to bottom. Spreading the operation wound open with a set of ratcheted retractors, I felt inside for the round lump. Bit by bit I pulled it close to the opening where I could see it. It was not part of any organ, but an independent, tense sphere containing some sort of thickish fluid and stuck at dozens of points to the loops of intestine. It was going to take a long time to free all those attachments. Beneath it might lie large blood vessels that I could not see; there might be weaknesses in the wall of the thing which would rupture as I separated it. I began cautiously and laboriously to break the adhesions with the handle of my scalpel, as using the sharp blade might pierce the sphere and release the contents, with appalling consequences. After half an hour I had still freed only a small part of the mass. On I went, stopping from time to time to check Billy's pulse, colour and breathing. He slept deeply. Two hours later I had freed all of the mass that I could see. Now for the underneath bit.

As I tried swinging the sphere over so that I could approach the lower adhesions less blindly, I noticed something that made my stomach turn. A pink-brown creamy liquid was beginning to seep up between my fingers. I swabbed it away hurriedly and looked closely. More of the stuff welled up. I gently pressed the spherical mass. It was less tense than before. Somehow, somewhere below it had begun to leak. The unpleasant pink-brown cream was running over Billy's intestines.

Cursing silently, I pressed on rapidly with the complete removal of the lump, now a collapsed and flabby bladder. With that gone, I surveyed the terrible sight before me: an abdominal cavity which was awash with pus full of amoebae and nasty bacteria. No matter what, Billy was going to have quite a case of peritonitis. How could I remove most of the foul stuff? If I put a drain into his tummy, as is done in humans, he would only pluck out the rubber tube when he came to. But would the wound hold if I stitched it with much of that rubbish inside?

Then I recalled watching as part of my surgery course at university an operation on a human patient whose gastric ulcer had burst just after being bombarded with a meal of steak pie, chips and peas, covering his liver, spleen, stomach and all the other bits and pieces of organs inside him with gravy, peas and chewed-up bits of food. The surgeon had not made a big fuss about this dinner that had gone so sadly astray but had dealt with it in a thoroughly down-to-earth, commonsense sort of way: he had ordered up two or three sterilized stainless-steel buckets full of warm saline solution and simply swilled out his patient's innards by pouring in a couple of gallons and letting it wash out. Then he had done it again, just as if he was washing down his garden path after a spot of untidy gardening. The peas and all the rest of the meal were washed away and what small quantities of foreign matter and bacteria remained in the abdominal cavity following this practical bit of laundry were easily controlled by antibiotics. I decided to use the same method. Sending Edith for some bottles of sterile saline solution, I sucked out as much of the pus as I could with a special tube and vacuum pump. When the saline was ready I used it to wash the intestines and surrounding organs, rinsed them again and again, popped everything back into place and sprinkled antibiotic powder in nooks and crevices. The rest was simple: stitching up the various layers of peritoneum, muscle, fat and skin.

Billy gradually began to come round when he was taken off the gas, but because of the phencyclidine still active in his body he would not be fully back to normal until the following day. Mrs. Lomax did not object when I insisted that Billy would have to go naked and unadorned until his operation wound healed; chimps' tissues heal rapidly when left dry and open to the oxygen in the air.

By the time Billy came to have his stitches out, he was his old fighting self once more. I did the job only when they had finally succeeded in slipping him some tranquillizer in a sweet plum, seven days after the date originally planned for the appointment. Billy had recovered excellently. There was no sign of peritonitis and he looked the picture of health. My examination of the pus from his lump had shown the presence of both amoebae and bacteria, as I had suspected, but these were dealt with by a course of fruit-flavoured drugs originally designed for children.

"By the way, Dr. Taylor," said Mrs. Lomax, when she brought Billy for his final check-up with her perspiring, pink-faced husband standing by, "this amoeba. Is there any chance that George here brought it home from the office?"

George mopped his forehead and looked appealingly at me, saying nothing.

"No chance, Mrs. Lomax," I replied firmly, "absolutely no chance."

George Lomax let out a sigh of happy relief. "Now, how much do we owe you, Dr. Taylor?" he asked.

10

Julius

It was a dark, wet night. The roads were empty and sheeted with rain as I drove home from a 3 a.m. call to an old cow whose calf had a head three sizes too big for her mother's pelvis. I had removed the big-headed infant by Caesarean and then, sticky, sweaty and covered with pieces of chaff, set off for a bath and what remained of the night's sleep. By nine o'clock that morning I would be at Belle Vue to begin a day's chiropody, trimming the overgrown hooves of every one of three dozen agile, unco-operative aoudads. Not my favourite occupation wrestling with those fellows, was my last thought as I fell asleep. Yes, today looked like being a hard one.

But I was learning that in zoo work it is impossible to plan ahead. As I sat bleary-eyed at breakfast, the telephone rang and the distant elfin voice of a frantic Tunisian animal importer delivered a message in a mixture of French and English over a line that crackled and howled like a banshee.

"Dr. Taylor, this is M. Taouche. Mr. Legge at Belle Vue told me where to contact you. *Please* come quick. I have twelve dying giraffes, ici en Tunisie!"

I stood looking through the persistent autumn drizzle at the cotton-mill chimneys impaling the low, early morning clouds hanging over the town, while M. Taouche told of the happenings on the farm near the town of Sbeitla, below the Atlas Mountains, where he had set up a quarantine station for African animals bound eventually for Europe. When his Arab keepers had risen that morning they had found that every one of the twelve magnificent Rothschild's giraffes on the farm was lying prostrate on the ground with legs askew, necks arched back and bellies bloated so grotesquely that the skin seemed about to split.

My mind whirred as I listened. I had only a few seconds before I must come up with advice that could give twelve helpless patients, unseen and unexamined fifteen hundred miles away, a fighting chance. This was ludicrous! How could I ever consider seriously working a one-man practice that might extend over half the globe? Some medical doctors will not take on patients living at the other side of the same town, yet here was I listening to a man paying ten dollars a minute in long-distance charges to plead for help. Come on, lad, I said to myself, this is what independent full-time zoo work would be all about. Every day things like this would be happening; was this not what I had always wanted? There had never really been any choice, had there? Cats with coughs and ponies with pleurisy had been the qualifying heats; the main race for me was supposed to be just this sort of situation. My mind cleared. No time to mull over a considered review of possibilities, diagnoses and prognostications. I had to learn the art of making snap decisions about critical situations in Cathay or Katmandu and always be right—or at least never harmfully wrong.

M. Taouche had finished his account of all he knew about the giraffes. Clearly the animals were bloated by gas produced by something they had eaten fermenting in their warm, wet stomachs. The gas pressure must be released before any distended stomach ruptured or pressed on the heart and stopped it.

"OK," I said, "I'll fly out at once. Meanwhile do this: get your man to find the biggest, broadest hypodermic needles he can—from a clinic or a doctor somewhere—and tell him to stick one into the swollen belly of each animal at its highest point on the left-hand—repeat, *left*-hand—side."

"Mais oui," came the Tunisian's faint voice, "but would it not be better for Abu al Ma'arri, my man, to release the pressure with a sharp knife?"

"No, repeat *no*! Do that and you will lose all the giraffes for sure!" I had seen too many cattle that had overgorged themselves on lush spring grass lanced in that way by farmers. Gas came out all right, but when the knife was withdrawn, the hole in the stomach moved away from the hole in the skin and the remaining gas forced stomach contents into the abdominal cavity. Peritonitis followed and none survived.

"One last thing," I continued. "If possible, see if your man can find some washing detergent."

The line hissed and crackled. "Washing detergent?"

"Yes. Tell him to give a teaspoonful of detergent powder—detergent, *not* soap—in water by mouth to each giraffe. He should be able to handle them if they're down and in such a bad way."

"But detergent powder in the stomach! It will froth, will it not? Like in my bath? Have I understood you correctly, Doctor? Detergent? Hein?"

"I repeat: detergent, d-e-t-e-r-g-e-n-t. Got it?"

The phone hissed more furiously than ever and the line went dead. I hurried to pack a bag while Shelagh dialled Air France. There was a plane to Paris from Manchester in ninety minutes, and in Paris I could pick up Tunisair. Shelagh followed me into the bedroom and stuck chunks of toast and grapefruit marmalade into my mouth while I used both hands to cram shirts, syringes, tins of emergency surgical equipment, drugs, dart-gun, toothpaste, mosquito cream, money belt, alarm clock and water-purifying tablets into a bulging grip. Also, never left behind, the dog-eared collected poems of John Betjeman.

"Ring Belle Vue, love, will you?" I said as I went out to the car. "The aoudads will have to wait for their chiropody.

Oh, and ring Norman Whittle. I know he'll be a bit browned off but would he do my surgery and the RSPCA clinic and could he be on instead of off duty this weekend. Tell him I'm off to Tunis to see a bunch of bloated giraffes."

"Leaving me to do the dirty work," she replied, making a face. "Norman won't be pleased. This means the end of his sailing on Lake Windermere on Sunday, and you know how he feels about the way you keep rushing off."

"My profuse apologies to him," I answered. "Oh, I almost forgot—just in case detergent powder is hard to get on the Algerian border, be a good girl and nip and fetch me your packet of Daz."

At Tunis airport a rotund little man in a white suit and pink tie stood by the arrival gate sweating profusely and holding aloft a piece of cardboard with my name crayoned on it. Beside him a tall black man wearing a crocheted skull cap and grimy grey jibba was mopping the perspiration from his companion's brow with a large silk handkerchief.

M. Taouche threw his cardboard away as I walked up to him. "Thank heavens you've arrived," he squeaked, shaking me vigorously by the hand. "No, I've no further news from the south, except Abu al Ma'arri thinks that the giraffes' trouble might be because of some peaches he fed them last night. He says the fruit was over-ripe when it arrived. Pour moi, I believe he has been selling the good fruit to the villagers near the farm and keeping only the worst for my animals. It's important you go down there tout de suite."

"But aren't you coming too?"

"Sadly, no. I want to, I need to, but I have important work here in Tunis. Anyway, I am sure that I personally could be of little assistance. Nasser here will drive you, and Abu and the other men will do anything you ask." He fidgeted with his tie with fingers like cocktail sausages.

"Let's go then," I replied. "We may be too late already, you realize. Giraffes don't usually last long once they're down."

M. Taouche's forehead oozed fresh sweat globules and Nasser blotted them up as we walked out to the parking lot. Nasser jumped into a pick-up truck and Taouche pumped my hand again. "Au revoir, Doctor," he said. "In'ch Allah, all will go well down south." Nasser and I set off on the long drive to the village near Sbeitla.

The journey was interminable. We travelled south at first, passing through lemon groves and tobacco fields glowing red-gold in the afternoon sunshine, then turned west, away from the Gulf of Hammamet, into a smoky twilight, rattling over mile after long mile of scrub and steppe. Every few hundred yards we would be brought to a juddering crawl by jay-walking flocks of sheep or goats, by donkey carts slewed across the road while their owners loaded bales of esparto grass, or by smoke-belching trucks weaving dangerously down the wrong side of the road. Darkness came suddenly, an indigo sky with a half moon dodging between tufts of cloud, and the truck started to climb up into the hills. It was too cold and too bumpy to sleep, and I could see little beyond the few square feet of grey dust picked out by the headlights. Nasser, having been disappointed to hear that no, I was not a relative of Elizabeth Taylor, had long since lapsed into silence. The only words to pass between us were an occasional "Imshi, imshi!" from me, a tentative stab at the Arabic equivalent of "Faster, faster!" It brought no perceptible increase in speed.

The low houses and narrow streets of Sbeitla showed no sign of light or life. We climbed on through winding valleys where the wind blew coarse dust into the open-sided pick-up and my eyes became sore with squinting. At last, ten hours after leaving Tunis, Nasser hauled the wheel over and we lurched off the road and ran down a rutted track. The head-lights picked out a group of white buildings set on three sides round a yard—the quarantine farm. Nasser skidded to a halt and shouted something in Arabic, and Abu al Ma'arri with his three companions came out of a doorway carrying kerosene lanterns. All wore jibbas and skull caps except for Abu, who sported a tattered old French army greatcoat. He had two black teeth remaining in an ever-smiling mouth, and a snow-white scar like forked lightning zigzagged across the cornea of each eye. Like one of my chimpanzee patients at Rhenen Zoo in Holland, he had six fingers on each hand. He introduced the others, Hussein, Abdul and another Abdul.

"Venons, where are the giraffes?" I said, anxious to get started.

Abu's happy face glinted in the soft glow of the oil lamps. His melon-slice smile broadened as he said in halting French, "Five are dead, Doctor. But seven live. I pricked them as you instructed." He led the way through the darkness to a rough wooden stockade behind one of the crumbling cement-block buildings.

The feeble light of the lanterns showed me a horrific scene. All on their sides, with limbs and necks in a higgledy-piggledy heap of unnatural and agonized positions, the giraffes sprawled like a collapsed log-pile. At first it was impossible to tell the dead from the living. All had swollen bellies.

I climbed over the fence and picked my way warily between the horizontal legs, but the flickering lantern made it difficult to avoid contact with the limbs. Accidentally I brushed against a hind leg. That animal was still alive. It gave a weak kick that had none of the pile-driver force that can disembowel a predator snapping incautiously at a giraffe's heels on the African plains, but it was enough to sweep both my legs from under me. On my knees I crouched and hunched my shoulders. There were five or six iron-hard hooves within inches of my head. Touch one of those again and I could be brained. With the delicate care of a man in a minefield I rose to my feet and continued my rounds of this charnel house-cum-hospital ward. Yes, there were seven animals still breathing. The mounts of small hypodermic needles sprouted from the belly walls of some of them. Despite my instructions to place them on the left side only— the point at which the stomach lies closest to the skin in giraffes—some needles gleamed in the lantern light on the animals' right sides. They were in the intestine and useless for releasing gas in the stomach.

The surviving animals bore their agonies with the mute fortitude typical of the dignity of my sort of patient. People often say giraffes have no voice. That is not strictly true; I have sometimes heard them give a short chirping cry. These poor creatures were utterly silent.

"Bring another lantern in and watch the feet," I shouted to Abu.

At last he understood and picked his way over to me. As he held both lanterns high, I picked one giraffe and, with a quick stab, stuck a special device for tapping off gas through the skin into the stomach. There was a flatulent puff of foul-smelling vapour from the instrument, the giraffe's belly subsided a little and then, to my dismay, a noisome khaki foam began to pour out. As I had feared, the gas in the stomachs was not in one giant bubble; it had produced a vast, fine froth that the animal could not burp. This was where the detergent came in. It would break up the foam in the animals' stomachs in the same way that a drop of detergent bubble-bath liquid will instantly destroy a soap foam.

"Did you give them detergent?" I asked the Arab.

"Detergent?" He looked puzzled.

"Poudre, poudre à laver—dans la bouche!" I struggled wretchedly with the words. Abu smiled broadly and shook his head.

I went round all the living animals and released what gas I could. All contained foam. Thank God for Shelagh's Daz, I thought, and prayed that, shocked and far gone as the giraffes were, I might be able to save at least some with my wife's washing powder. I mixed a little with water in a wine bottle. To Hussein and Abdul number one I said slowly, "Hold the head of the giraffe. I give this drink." I gesticulated and they understood. "Manchester United," said Hussein, for no apparent reason. From Greenland to Indonesia, wherever I work, I always meet at least one person whose English extends to soccer terms, usually "Manchester United", the most famous soccer team in the zoological world. The man who catches the first yeti and brings it to me for a check-up will say, if nothing else, "Manchester United".

One by one I drenched the giraffes with the detergent mixture. Now to tackle the intoxicating effects of the foodstuffs fermenting in the giraffes' stomachs. I shot high-potency vitamin B directly into the bloodstream, the treatment applied to humans who became hospital patients after swigging a bottle of whisky in an hour or so. A heavily pregnant female was one of those still alive. Cautiously I made an internal examination and felt the calf kick in his comfortable water bed. It was amazing that it, or indeed any of the giraffes, was still putting up a fight.

I could do no more that night. Abu al Ma'arri led the way to my quarters. "Please, Doctor, I hope you will be comfortable here." He showed me into a small room which had no door and was bare except for a straw-filled mattress on the floor, two carefully folded blankets and a picture of President Bourguiba on the wall. The other occupant of the room was a gecko, with a body like a smouldering crusty heap of jewels. He scuttled behind President Bourguiba as Nasser brought me a bowl of greasy water in which to wash and a jam jar full of strong sweet tea. In the light of a lantern I washed, dried myself on my shirt, drank the tea and arranged myself uncomfortably under the blankets. From the Arabs' room came laughter and murmurs of admiration as Abu demonstrated his prowess at catching rats with his bare hands and his ability to pop live scorpions into his mouth, roll them about with his tongue and slowly extrude them sting first, unharmed and unruffled, onto the palm of his hand. Despite the noise, the cold and the blankets' reek of goat and garlic and sweat, I was soon in a deep sleep.

The next morning I was up early. One more of my patients had died during the night; the remaining six were no longer lying on their sides but sitting up on their briskets. The bellies of five, including the pregnant female, were no longer resonant like drums when I tapped them but the sixth was still very blown out. While the men dragged out the cadavers of the six dead giraffes, I went round again in the grey light before dawn giving more vitamin B and circulatory stimulants as well. By sun-up most of the animals were looking distinctly better and I started paying attention to the "bedsores" on the recumbent creatures. The still-distended sixth animal I drenched again in the hope of avoiding more drastic surgery.

Giving the drench some time to act, I looked round the dilapidated farm. Dirt was everywhere, and a long sloping dung heap ran right up to the round stone well at which Nasser and the others drew water by means of a bucket on a rope. There was a smell of manure and burnt wood. As I sat with my back against a wall, letting the sun warm my face, I heard a screeching noise from one corner of the yard. The Arabs were gathered round what looked like a dog kennel, watching intently and chattering as Hussein bent over the kennel with a stick in his hand. Abu was laughing happily and clapping his six-fingered hands. The screech came again. I could not identify it. Pig? No. Cat? Whatever it was, it did something to the hairs at the back of my neck. I stood up and walked over to the knot of men. They looked round as I arrived and parted to give me room to see.

Hussein stood in front of a wooden box with a door made

of stout iron bars. Proudly he re-introduced his stick between the bars and jabbed fiercely at the interior. There was another awful screech, a scrabbling noise and a thumping and a banging from inside the box. I bent down and looked inside. The most tragic animal face that I have ever seen confronted me. The box contained a hyena. Almost as big as the container itself and with no room to turn round, there stood a full-grown striped hyena, trembling, panting, open-jawed, with every visible tooth freshly broken, one eye wide with frenzy, the other a bloody mass. His neck and forelegs were a mass of cuts and sores, his ears were torn and bleeding. By my side, Hussein thrust the stick into the box and ground it into the cheek of the hyena. It turned its head as far as it could, but no matter how it tried it could not retreat from the cruel point. "Tottenham Hotspur," crowed Hussein.

I felt my head drain of blood and my face prickle with cold anger. I straightened up and opened my mouth. I wanted to shout something, anything. Not a sound came out. The Arabs looked at me and grinned pleasantly.

"Bad dog," said Abu, leading me to the back of the hyena's prison. There were more bars there. The animal's hind-quarters showed the same loathsome lacerations as his head.

Hussein came round with his stick. "Kick off," he said, and pointed to the hyena's hock joints. I saw what he felt so proud about; the poor beast had been hamstrung. The Achilles tendons on both legs had been severed by a sharp instrument.

I stood with my back to the bars so that Hussein could not introduce his stick again. My voice returned trembling. "What do you bloody well think you're doing?" I wished I knew the worst Arabic or even French obscenities.

"Bad dog," said Abu again, his smile growing. "He kills chickens. Dirty. Smells. No good."

"Not bad dog," I said, wishing I could vomit the words. "Why do you wound him? Pourquoi blesser?"

All the Arabs laughed gently. Abu's two black teeth were bared as he explained politely, "But Doctor, to teach him. To teach him. A good idea for a bad dog, n'est-ce pas?"

Hussein, blocked from his victim by my legs, went round to the front of the box again. I roared, dashed after him and grabbed the stick from his hands. "No you don't!" I shouted, and broke the stick over my knee. "Rien va plus!" I picked up the halves of stick and broke them again and again until I found it impossible to destroy the small bits further with my fingers. The Arabs watched. Abu smiled. Hussein glared sullenly, then kicked viciously at the hyena's box and walked away. The others followed. I crouched in front of the terrified animal and looked deep into his one eye. He must have been a maverick, trapped when he left a pack in the hills to come foraging on the farm. There was nothing I could do for him. Both ends of the box were secured by rusty padlocks and even if I could have got to him, severed Achilles tendons are a major injury in man and domestic animals, not to mention wild creatures.

An hour later the giraffes were continuing to improve except for the one whose stomach was still swollen. I decided to operate and literally unload the offending food. It was my first major operation on a giraffe, a notoriously difficult species to anaesthetize safely even today in the best of animal parks, but I injected it with a stiff dose of tranquillizer, then numbed a large T-shaped area over the left abdominal wall with local anaesthetic. Abu and the others drifted over to watch as I disinfected the skin and cut through to the stomach. It was full of stinking fruit and vegetables, and the overpowering smell of alcoholic peaches confirmed the cause of the distended bellies. With my bare hand and arm I reached deep into the digesting broth, cupped my palm and ladled out handful after handful of the stuff, making sure as I cast it aside that some would accidentally splatter my audience's jibbas. Then I placed a small quantity of penicillin into the remaining stomach contents to knock out over-enthusiastic fermenting bacteria and stitched up. But as I threaded my needle, positioned the layers of muscle and skin with my forceps and swept the persistent flies from the operation site I could think of only one thing: the hyena.

That night I sat alone on the floor of my room to eat my supper of mutton stew and pitta bread. The giraffes were almost forgotten as I agonized over the plight of the hyena. If I broke the padlocks off the kennel, the poor beast could not get anywhere. I knew the Arabs were giving him food and water occasionally; he was likely to stay alive for their cruel amusement for weeks. Then the answer came to me.

By eleven o'clock the Arabs had gone to bed. The farm was quiet except for the occasional bleat of a goat and the restless murmurings of drowsing pigeons. After an hour or so I lit my lantern, took what I needed from my bag and tiptoed out into the yard. No one stirred. Holding the lantern high to avoid slipping into the dung heap, I quietly approached the hyena's box. I could hear him breathing tensely in the darkness and could imagine his pulse beginning to race and his shoulder hairs bristling as he sensed my approach. I pulled the syringe and injection bottle from my pocket, filled the syringe and blew out the lantern. Going round to the back of the box, I put a hand gently through the bars and felt a quivering ham muscle. The hyena growled lightly. Quickly I jabbed the hypodermic into his ham and pressed the plunger. He gave a short screech and I pulled away the empty syringe. I looked round; no one had been roused by the sound of the "bad dog."

I crept swiftly back to my room without relighting my lantern, so I did not see the dung heap until I walked into it. I did not mind, for as I sat on my mattress decontaminating my shoes with cotton wool, I knew that the hyena would by now have passed painlessly into oblivion. Rarely in zoo work do I have to destroy an animal; even with modern humane methods it is unpleasant work, bringing death to a living creature. But giving a shot of lethal T61

12

to the hyena that dark North African night was one of the most fulfilling things I have ever done as a veterinarian.

Next day the giraffes were improving still, and the one on which I had operated was catching the others up fast. I gave more injections, and by the second afternoon I was delighted to see that all bar one, the pregnant female, were on their feet. They were groggy and only picked at the hay I had told the men to give them, but at least they were up. "When a giraffe goes down," Matt Kelly used to tell me, "he never

ever gets up." The pregnant female was running with milk and making determined but unsuccessful attempts to rise. With any luck I could get away in a couple of days.

The third morning, going round the back of the farm buildings in the direction of the unpleasant hole in the rocks that was our toilet, I nearly walked straight into a tethered group of six camels, each with a large bundle of esparto grass on its back. The nearest spat balefully in my direction. Beyond them, Abu al Ma'arri and the others were talking intently to four other men, dressed like themselves in jibbas and skull caps. As I approached, the strangers began talking furiously in Arabic, addressing their remarks to Abu and looking suspiciously at me.

"Salaam aleikùm," I said.

Only Abu answered, his smile flickering uncertainly. "Aleikum salaam, Doctor. You come for breakfast? Nasser will make tea presently and bring it to you."

The camel men stood silently staring at me. I certainly was not going to obey the call of nature with this lot watching.

"Merci," I replied. "After that we must begin darting the giraffes." The animals were no longer safe to inject by hand, except the pregnant female, and I would administer the necessary drugs by dart-gun.

I walked back to the yard, wondering uneasily what the Arabs and their new cronies had been nattering about. Twenty minutes later Nasser appeared with the tea. I drank it while I loaded my 10cc darts with chemicals, then went to look at the animals. The zebras were eating a new consignment of food the lorry had brought in yesterday, the rhinos were still sleeping and the giraffes looked in fine fettle. None of the puncture holes in their bellies seemed to be going the wrong way and the operation wound on the one animal was healing neatly. I was as pleased as Punch. The mother-to-be was sitting up alertly and chewing her cud. Maybe today she would be up.

Suddenly there was a horrible strident scream. My first thought was, what the hell are they torturing now? But this sounded like a human and it came from behind the buildings, where the camels were. I ran out of the yard and round the corner. All the Arabs, Abu's band and the strangers, were gathered round the head of a standing camel. Two men were hanging tightly onto its leather bridle as it bucked and gurgled. Nearby Abu whirled round and round, hopping on one foot like a dervish. It was he who had screamed, I saw, for with his good left hand he clutched the wrist of his right, a pulped and bloody mass from which two of the six fingers dangled down, attached only by shreds of skin. As I watched in amazement the camel suddenly reared up, arched its neck and, with a bubbling roar, spat out from its mouth a flat oblong object about the same size and shape as a tobacco pouch. One of the camel men swiftly snatched it up and dropped it down the neck of his jibba, but not before I had time to see that it was made of oilskin and was neatly tied with cord. Every one of the men, except Abu, who continued his distressed dance, had his eyes fixed on me. Suddenly I realized what was in the pouch and how Abu had come to have his fingers ground between the powerful molars of a camel. Fear took a firm hold of my stomach and gouged deep. I had just glimpsed a rare, hidden, evil thing, the bungling of one link in a long and filthy chain that stretched from the poppy fields of Asia to the junkies of Times Square and Piccadilly Circus.

Abu's greatcoat was now soaking with blood. The men made no move towards him. They just stood looking at me. Pointing at Abu, I said, "Doctor. Médecin très nécessaire!"

Abu stopped gyrating and looked at me. He was not smiling. "Non," he said firmly. "I will come to your room presently for attention."

"But . . ." I began.

"I cannot go to the doctor," interrupted the injured man. Hussein stepped forward and I froze to my marrow as he slowly pointed at me and then, with the same finger, drew a line across his throat. "Offside," he said. "Penalty kick."

Dizzy with fright, I went back to my room and took from my instrument box the largest scalpel I had. Wrapping a wad of cotton wool round the cutting end, I stuck it securely down my sock under cover of my right trouser leg. It was sheer fright, not melodramatic imagination, that spurred me on as I rammed a wicked-looking rhinoceros needle on the end of a 10cc flying syringe down the barrel of the dart-pistol. Its sharp point poked from the muzzle. Locking the breech, I cocked the pistol at full gas pressure. Then I sat on my mattress and laid the puny weapon within easy reach. I reflected that one of the lesser, but to me saddest, miseries in the whole squalid affair was that it was yet another example of the satanic ingenuity with which Man is prepared to destroy innocent fellow creatures in furthering his own ends. Those grumpy, imperious, fascinating camels tethered outside were unwitting couriers of vice. Once safely across the border into Algeria, they would be slaughtered and the precious cargo retrieved from their stomachs. I almost wished there might be some crooked veterinarian in the pay of the traffickers who, by an operation similar to the one I had performed on the giraffe, could recover the oilskin packages less wastefully.

Abu broke into these bizarre daydreams by appearing at the door of my room. I leapt to my feet, dart-gun in hand, but his face was haggard and he silently held out his bitten fingers.

"You need a hospital or doctor, you know," I told him.

He shook his head vigorously. "No. You can do it. Have you not treated one camel bitten by another?" He stared hard at me. "Do it and forget it. It is nothing." Then, deliberately spacing his words, "It—is—nothing. Please remember that."

The menace behind Abu's words hung in the air as I cleaned up the stumps of the pair of fingers. I was preparing what little I had in the way of dressings when there was a shout from outside. Abdul number two came dashing in and jabbered excitedly in Arabic. Abu said, "The giraffe with calf—she has got up but has crashed down again."

Leaving Abu, I pushed through the knot of camel men who must have been watching the door of my room and dashed round to the giraffe stockade. There against the wooden fence lay the female, her legs still and her neck hideously twisted. She was not breathing and her eyes had the languorous gaze into infinity that I knew too well. She was dead. In falling she had broken her neck on the top rail of the fence. Stunned, I stood for a split second and then shouted to Nasser, who had come running, "Quick, a knife. *Vite!*"

Like a magician, from under his jibba he produced a sharp stiletto. I took it, jumped over the fence and, running over to the dead giraffe, for the first time in my life performed the original Caesarean operation. With a long, raking slash the womb was revealed, bulging between still flickering muscle sheets. I grabbed its glistening outer surface, steadied it, then cut again quickly and carefully. I thrust my hand in and felt a warm, slippery forelimb. With no time or need for elegance, I held the leg tightly and gave a great heave. The ungainly, tangled body of a baby giraffe rose into the sunlight through the lengthening split in the womb. I plopped it down onto the earth and stood gasping with the effort. The little form twitched. I knelt down and felt the heart. It was beating!

With a wild shout I picked up its hind legs and stood it on its nose to clear its mouth and nostrils. I slapped its chest, there was a sneeze, and an eyelid fringed with the most glamorously long lashes outside Hollywood fluttered. I called Nasser to help me pick up the heavy creature once again and we shook it with all our might. Down again. Up again. More slapping of the chest and then suddenly, wonderfully, the little calf was breathing stickily but strongly.

Caesar himself had been born, it was said, in just this manner, an orphan from the womb. This little fellow was going to live, and I christened him Julius on the spot. He wriggled and sat up. His large round dark eyes looked at me, and I wondered whether, like ducks, baby giraffes are imprinted and emotionally bound to the first living creature they see.

The whimsy that Julius might be inclined to call me "Momma" vanished as I heard voices behind me. Looking round I saw the camel men talking to Hussein and Nasser. They seemed angry, and one of them pointed briefly in my direction. In the excitement of Julius's arrival I had forgotten other, darker things. With what I hoped was a disarmingly cheerful wave, I called out, "The baby is hungry. I must take him to my room and feed him," and began to half carry, half drag the struggling giraffe in the direction of the yard. My heart bounded as Julius and I staggered round the corner. The yard was empty and there was Nasser's pick-up truck parked by the dung heap—with the keys in. Without ceremony I hauled the baby across the uneven ground and pushed him like a sack of potatoes over the tailgate of the open vehicle. Furtively looking round to check that there was still no one about, I took off my jacket, wrapped it round Julius's legs and firmly tied the sleeves together.

Then, with adrenalin flooding through my veins, I ran into my room, grabbed the dart-gun and my grip and dashed back to the truck, dropping bottles of medicine, artery forceps and other bits of equipment on the way. I did not turn back for them, but as I was about to leap into the driving seat my eye caught the metal pot of mutton stew for the midday meal simmering on a wood fire outside the Arabs' room. As if by instinct I reached into the grip and fumbled for my small tin of Altan, a powerful horse and zebra purgative that looks like cayenne pepper and has very little taste. Still I was alone in the yard. A moment later,

Abu al Ma'arri and his friends had enough Altan in their meal to produce dramatic effects in four draught horses, and I hoped they would pass a distressing and cathartic twenty-four hours.

"Compliments of one hyena, you bastards," I shouted as I threw away the empty tin and ran yet again to the truck where Julius lay uncomplaining and wide-eyed. Safely aboard, I turned on the ignition and pressed the starter button. The engine fired and I let out the clutch with a bang. With wheels spinning in a shower of grit, dust and manure we shot forward and charged out of the yard and up the rutted track. Ten minutes later, with a little giraffe sucking gently on my right ear, I roared through the main street of Sbeitla. With only one stop for fuel, Julius and I went flat out for Tunis.

Half a day later, weary and covered in dust, I was in the office of Herr Mueller, the surprised curator of Tunis Zoo. Julius needed expert rearing and with luck I would be on the next plane for Paris. "Take good care of him," I said before I left. "He's my boy!"

I just had time to call on M. Taouche in his lemon-blossom-scented garden and to tell my story to my client. When I came to the bit about Abu al Ma'arri and how he went back to having ten fingers like the rest of us, M. Taouche closed his eyes and chewed energetically on his cheroot. Whether he was involved with the sinister affair I could only guess. He said nothing except to thank me and to promise me a bonus along with my fee when I rendered my account. That account was never paid: three weeks later M. Taouche died of a heart attack.

I I

Of Bishops and Babies

Christianity, unlike some of the world's other great religions, has no particular theology of animals. After establishing that the Deity constructed whales and other marine creatures on the fifth day and turned his attention to terrestrial fauna on the sixth, it has fussed and feuded pretty exclusively over one often rather unattractive and unreliable species of naked ape. True, Thomas Aquinas split scholarly hairs over the nature of the brutish soul, and Francis would have been on the Assisi branch committee of the RSPCA if there had been such a thing in the twelfth century; but Protestant bishops can be run to earth in the huntin', shootin', fishin' fraternity, devout Orthodox peasants of the Mediterranean trap small songbirds by the million, Latin Catholics leave Mass to attend the ritual torture of black bulls on a Sunday afternoon. I find it odd. The more I have studied, looked at and handled animals, seen their intrinsic beauty, the perfection with which they spin their strands in the web of life, the more I have tilted towards a unified theology of all living creatures, the scorpion and the maggot just as much as the tiger or the whale. Dead, beneath my autopsy knife, they reveal not just themselves but also what I am: part of the all-purposeful, all-beautiful, endless wheel of growth and change, of death and regeneration. Nothing is chaos. Look close, with seeing eyes, and even a blob of pus is a wondrous, active, ordered microcosm.

The Church of England often exhibits a rather dotty concern for animals, however, which I experienced soon after my return from Tunisia when a vicar friend of mine in a country parish across the Pennines in Yorkshire invited me to read the lesson at a special church service for pets. The occasion was graced by the presence of a bishop, who preached a sermon full of round plummy aphorisms about sparrows and their welfare-state existence, Daniel's way with big cats and how much happier we all would be if we lived like armadilloes, although for the life of me I could not make out what it was about these nocturnal miniature tanks that so impressed the gaitered cleric as epitomizing the Christian ideal. To illustrate his point he produced a small, curled-up representative of the species from beneath his purple cassock. It had been borrowed from a nearby zoo, and its dramatic appearance had an electrifying effect on the chancel full of nodding choirboys.

Unfortunately His Lordship mishandled the armour-plated ball and dropped it, whereupon it rolled down the pulpit steps, galvanizing the choirboys still more. A full complement leapt unceremoniously from their seats in both front rows and scrabbled to retrieve the creature, which made off towards the organ. The armadillo won by a short head, nipped behind the forest of pipes and was not seen again until halfway through Evensong a week later.

The young congregation would never have guessed from the bishop's admonition, "In being kind to beasts we are honouring the work of God's hands," that the reverend gentleman hunted two days a week and was the proud possessor of a well-used pair of Purdey shotguns. There were children with dogs and cats, budgies and rabbits. Some clustered outside the porch with their ponies. Doting parents, sly-eyed schoolboys with grass snakes in jars and toads in their pockets, girls clutching goldfish bowls, all sat side by side in the pews of the seventeenth-century stone church. There was one lad with a monkey, a chunky, muscle-bound pig-tailed macaque. It continually raised its eyebrows towards the preacher in the typical mildly challenging grimace of macaques, which made it seem like a sceptical, possibly agnostic listener. Its owner kept a firm grip on the leash with which it was restrained.

Blessing animals is, I suppose, a cut above doing the same thing to motor bikes or lawn mowers. Services for pets at least provide the small boys who attend such gatherings with the hope that something might turn up. On this occasion it already had, and the absconding armadillo brought back memories of forfeiting my place on the annual choir outing to Blackpool: a white mouse released under the long blue cassock of a middle-aged lady chorister at St. Edmund's Church had resulted in the unusual spectacle of the lady vaulting clean over the choir stall in the middle of the reading of the banns and streaking off into the vestry.

". . . and so I leave you with these words. Kindness, patience, goodwill to all creatures, not least the wonderful creatures that bring us so much joy. In the name of the Father" etc, etc. The bishop came to the end of his address. A final hymn was sung and everyone trooped outside. The bishop was going to move among the crowd assembled in the churchyard and bless the beasts—human and otherwise.

In the churchyard it was warm and sunny. My part in the proceedings was over. I stood watching the milling crowd and saying good-bye to the vicar before making my way back over the hills to Rochdale. The bishop was in a jolly, expansive mood as he wandered through the chattering throng, his right hand raised in benediction. He cooed to the budgies thrust up towards his face, tugged the ears of some of the dogs and had his picture taken as he sat perilously on a donkey. All at once the boy who had brought the macaque barged through the crowd waving a leather leash, at the end of which there was no sign of a monkey. The press of jostling humans and animals parted like the Red Sea before Moses as a squat brown figure bounded between them. The pig-tailed macaque shot down the church path, through the ancient lych-gate and straight through the partly open window of a sparkling new Bentley parked directly outside. He was pursued by his owner, closely followed by all the small boys present, and behind came the rest of us.

Inside the car the monkey was having a fine time. He quickly pulled open the door of the glove compartment and spilled out all the contents. A tin of pipe tobacco lying on the front seat was thrown out of the window, and the plastic cover of the interior light was prized off and bitten in two.

"Harry!" shouted the monkey's owner. "Stop that and come here!" He opened the car door a fraction.

Harry bared his wicked-looking canine teeth, grimaced as histrionically as any villain of Japanese theatre, and savagely bit the right hand of his owner as it moved towards him. Bleeding profusely and in obvious pain, the gallant lad advanced his other hand. Harry grabbed it, pulled it up to his jaws and lacerated the palm with a slash of his fangs. The poor boy fell back and the door was slammed to. The vicar led the casualty away.

By now the bishop had pushed through the crowd. "I say," he said, his genial expression fading fast, "that's my car, you know." He looked through the window at the macaque, which by now was flying round the interior like an angry bluebottle in a jam jar. "We really ought to get the chappie out of there." No one volunteered.

Then Harry spotted the dashboard, a surface bristling with interesting knobs and levers, glinting bits of chrome, plastic and glass. Just beneath the dashboard was an inviting twist of coloured wire which the inquiring mind of the would-be engineer could not ignore. As he reached down and pulled it there was a satisfying click, and the panel covering the tangle of assorted gadgetry behind the dashboard fell away.

"We must get that monkey out of my car," said the bishop, pale but calm.

The jungle of gleaming electronics now exposed fascinated Harry. With one powerful leathery hand he grasped a bunch of wires and plugs and pulled. They came away and bits of metal and plastic tinkled onto the floor. The electric clock stopped.

Harry looked at the bishop, raised his eyebrows sceptically and pressed the horn button. As its wires had just been disconnected it did not work. Harry pulled and the horn button broke off. He threw it out of the window.

"Please, sir, you haven't blessed Chirpy yet," said a little girl, worming her way through to the bishop's side and straining upwards with a fistful of budgerigar.

"Hrumph," said His Lordship.

Meanwhile I was marvelling at the speed with which a small monkey was dismantling a solidly built vehicle. If a gang of Harrys could be trained to work as fast assembling the various pieces of metalwork that now lay around the inside of the car, the labour problems of the automobile industry would be a thing of the past.

"Somebody do something! This bloody monkey is tearing my car apart!"

"Please, sir, you haven't done Chirpy," persisted the little girl, her budgerigar by now almost suffocated in her grip.

"Next year, next year!" shouted the bishop, purple-faced now as well as purple-robed. He patted the child so hard on the head that I expected to see her reel away cross-eyed.

I must confess I had thoroughly enjoyed the unique experience. The inside of the car was now in utter ruin. Harry was sitting in the back seat, looking round for anything he might have missed. Stirring myself, I decided I must do something. Pig-tailed macaques are one of the toughest and most dangerous species of monkey, and to tackle one single-handed in the close confines of a car would be foolhardy. I had no dart-gun with me, but I did have some anaesthetic in my car and plenty of syringes. I sent the vicar's wife to fetch a banana while I inspected the partly opened car window. The gap had been big enough for Harry to get in, so he could get out as well if he wished, and I could not wind the window up without opening the door. I sent a choirboy into the church for one of the thick hassocks, or kneeling pads. "Now," I said when he returned, "get up on the roof of the car just above the window, and when I give you the word jam the hassock hard down over the side."

Enthusiastically the boy scrambled up the gleaming paintwork. The bishop leaned against the lych-gate groaning, a hand across his eyes.

I held a piece of banana through the window. Harry sniffed at it, passed it as undoctored and ate it. It tasted good. I proffered another piece, holding it just outside the window gap. Harry slowly put his hand out to take it. "Jam it down!" I yelled to the boy on the roof as I seized Harry's hand and pulled with all my strength. Harry screamed and struggled vigorously but the boy with the hassock had narrowed the gap enough to stop me pulling an agitated twenty-five pounds of steely muscle and teeth completely out of the car. In half a second I had plunged the hypodermic into Harry's arm and whammed down the plunger. I released my grip and Harry retreated onto the rear window ledge, hollering furiously. In two minutes he began to drool, his eyes became dreamy and he emptied his bowels over the bishop's top hat. In another two minutes it was all over; Harry fell into a drowsing heap on the back seat and I opened the door to pull him out. We had been lucky— he would never be taken in that way again.

There was no hope of getting the bishop's car to start. It had to be towed to the next town for major repairs. I offered to drop His Lordship at the station on my way home.

"Many thanks, Doctor," he said as I stopped outside the ticket office. "Wouldn't have your job for the world. Damned brutes!"

If the Right Reverend gentleman's last two words are literally true, Old Nick is going to have a hell of a time dealing with Harry one of these days.

Despite my experience with the bishop and his Bentley, in the normal run of things I do not have to cross swords with the Established Church. With other faiths things can be different. There are many Moslem Pakistani folk living in the north of England, and at certain religious festivals they slaughter lambs. The rules lay down that the sacrifices must on no account be eaten by human beings, but it is perfectly acceptable for the lambs to be fed to wild beasts. At these times vans containing beautifully dressed and wholesome carcasses arrive at zoos and Pakistani gentlemen request that the meat be fed to the big cats. Solemnly the lamb is unloaded into the meat store and the van driver goes away, happy in the knowledge that the tenets of the faith have been upheld. Later, nominally Christian zoo keepers can be seen assembling in the zoo kitchen, armed with meat saws and cleavers and ready to decide who gets what for their family's Sunday joints.

The Moslem calendar was pinned up in the office of one head keeper whose animals I treated, with red lines marking the weeks when the staff could be sure to dine daily on mutton. Even the youngest assistant keeper of the Pets' Corner could tell you when Ramadan ended, although I doubt if he even knew what month Easter was in. Beside the head keeper's calendar were pinned two other pieces of paper. One listed the staff in order of precedence for the share-out:

Zoo director:	Loin, 2 shoulders, 2 legs, breast
Veterinarian:	2 shoulders, 2 legs, also likes kidneys, breast
Head keeper:	2 shoulders, 1 leg, liver, breast
Asst head keeper:	1 leg, kidneys
Head bird keeper:	4 cutlets
Reptile keeper:	1 cutlet, head

and so on down to:

Trainee keeper:	liver.

The other piece of paper was most important. When the lamb came, it came in abundance, and the head keeper was hard put to it to see that his staff's taste for the meat did not become jaded. It read:

Suggestions for all staff:

Mondays:	Lamb Argenteuil
Tuesdays:	Carré d'agneau Dordonnaise
Wednesdays:	Lamb Kashmir
Thursdays:	Kebabs
Fridays:	Navarin of lamb
Saturdays:	Lamb and vegetable casserole
Sundays:	Epigrammes d'agneau

N.B. Recipes for the above can be had from Nellie in the cash office.

Nellie kept a pile of duplicated instructions, for which useful service she received a choice roasting shoulder from the head keeper every Saturday during the sacrificing season.

Came the sad day when one of the Pakistani meat donors forgot his gloves and returned to the zoo stores shortly after making a delivery. Inside he found a dozen amateur butchers merrily dividing the spoils according to the list of precedence under the eagle eye of the head keeper. The scene that ensued, with the Pakistani snatching up a chopper and advancing hysterically on the red-faced sacrilegists, could have been the start of a holy war. Luckily the zoo director made an opportune appearance (coming to collect the ingredients for his favourite crown roast with cranberry stuffing) and the matter was temporarily shelved.

Some days later a polite Pakistani called at my home and introduced himself as the imam of the community whose sacrifice had been profaned by the zoo. Wild beasts were not particularly common in the north of England, at least not ones big enough to devour whole sheep carcasses, so the zoos were an essential means of disposal. Dumping on the municipal rubbish tip or incineration were out of the question. Could I advise him professionally?

Much as I had enjoyed my illicit share of meat, I was ethically bound to give him the best possible advice. "When you have sacrified the lambs," I said, "splash some non-poisonous green vegetable dye over the carcasses. That will not harm lions and tigers but will render the meat unappetizing to humans."

The imam thought for a moment. "Yes, I can recommend that to my people. Such colouring will not defile the sacrifice."

It was settled. Supplies of sacrificed lambs to the zoo resumed. The big cats enjoyed the new arrangements and the threat of a jehad erupting in the zoo grounds receded. But the head keeper and his staff had the very devil of a job cutting any uncoloured meat out of the carcasses, and I noticed that the precedence list in his office had been altered. Now the very bottom entry on the list read:

Veterinarian: 1 kidney (if any left over).

The zoo which narrowly escaped being decimated by a holy war was one of several in the north of England which I was by now visiting regularly. Belle Vue was still my major zoo client, however, as it had been throughout the five years since I took over the care of its animals from Norman Whittle, and there Matt Kelly had noticed something odd about the way Simba, a four-month-old lion cub, was moving.

Simba led a happy, carefree life with his parents and brothers and sisters until one day, for no obvious reason, his father suddenly bit him on the back. The wound did not look bad, just a pair of small puncture holes in the skin, but the cub started to become wobbly on his hind legs. When Matt called me in I found from an X-ray of Simba's back that he was becoming steadily paralysed; one of the adult lion's teeth had penetrated down to his backbone and a spinal abscess had developed.

I anaesthetized Simba and took him back to Rochdale in my car and there explored the area deep in the lumbar region of his spine, where the dirty tooth had set up a nasty pocket of diseased, pus-filled bone. With a scalpel and a special spoon-shaped gouge I removed the infected bone and put a small rubber drain tube into the wound. Stitched up, Simba looked like an inflatable toy lion with a red rubber valve projecting out of the middle of his back, ready for someone to attach a bicycle pump. Now for a long period of post-operative nursing; Simba was partially paralysed and incontinent, symptoms which would not go overnight. I needed somewhere to hospitalize him where I could keep a personal eye on him, and it was Shelagh who came up with the answer.

Our home in Rochdale, a Jacobean stone farmhouse on the edge of the moor, had one acre of walled market garden attached. Shelagh decided to build a lion hospital there. To the passer-by, and eventually to the tax-man, who considered the lion hospital a poor cover story to use in industrial Lancashire when we were claiming the building expenses, it looks like a wooden garden shed. It is now the home of Henry, my favourite and most intelligent goat, who no doubt considers it a perfect goat shed. It was erected, however, Henry and the tax man notwithstanding, as a bona fide, custom-built lion hospital. There Simba would be nursed back to health and to full use of his limbs and bladder.

This was the sort of thing Shelagh loves. While I attended to the medical side, giving the daily injections and checking the reflexes, Shelagh was Simba's nurse, physiotherapist, cook, companion and latrine attendant all rolled into one. Every two hours she meticulously bathed the protesting cub in baby soap and water so that his hind parts would not become sore because of his incontinence, dried him on one of a specially commandeered bunch of my bath towels and smeared the vulnerable areas with silicone ointment. Nourished on an appetizing steak tartare mixture that had me drooling at the mouth, and encouraged to use his legs outside on the grass when it was fine, Simba gradually mended.

In these days when lion cubs are cheaper than ten a penny, when the boxes they are carried in cost more than themselves and they are worth a hundred times more as a dead

skin than they could possibly be alive, it is sad to reflect that the very success of breeding and safely rearing lion cubs in zoos and safari parks over recent years has made some lion owners regard these big cats as characterless and as expendable as sausages out of a machine. I know they are lazy fellows but, like every other animal, the more you know them the more fascinating their ways and workings are seen to be. That was something Shelagh and I quickly learnt from Simba.

After a summer of Shelagh's physiotherapy, and to the relief of the farm cats who could not pursue voles in the market garden without finding themselves the quarry of a gleefully growling creature with sandy hair and enormous paws, it was time for the fully recovered lion to go back to the zoo. First I took him to make his and my debut on television. We were going to be interviewed about the cub's paralysis and subsequent recovery.

It became obvious when I led him into the studios on a dog lead that Simba, by now grown to an impressive size, was by no means filled with awe at passing the portals of the Temple of the Holy Box. An extra in full costume and make-up as a Roman senator came fussing down a corridor towards us. Busy primping himself in a small hand mirror, he had not noticed the lion ambling along by my side. His sandalled feet came level with us and Simba decided it was time for a bit of provocative rough-housing. As the senator passed, the lion clubbed with sheathed claws at the back of his knees, buckling them and bringing him crashing to the floor in a flurry of toga and velveteen jockey briefs. Apologizing, I helped the unharmed but fluttering actor to his feet. Then he saw Simba sitting blandly on his haunches waiting for me to resume our exploration.

"Ooh, my God, darling, what's that?" he exclaimed, clutching me with both hands like a scrawny vulture. "Have props brought a real lion in for the *Julius Caesar?*" He scurried off, theatrically casting the loose end of his toga over his shoulder.

We found the studio where the interviewer was waiting for us. Simba did not like the lights nor the way the sound man seemed to tease him with the boom microphone, swinging it to and fro above his head. It was just out of reach; perhaps, Simba thought, it was some sort of game. He decided to find out. With a great leap upwards he managed to get one set of claws on the microphone before the sound man could whisk it away. The wire-gauze casing of the microphone crashed to the floor. Simba looked up with watery eyes; not a bad game, this.

When I eventually settled in my seat with the lion at my side, Simba had a call of nature. Waddling away from me into the middle of the floor, he squatted and relieved his bowels. Within moments the studio reeked with the heavy and unforgettable odour of lion droppings. I retrieved the animal and asked for a shovel and bucket. "Don't worry yourself," they told me, "it will be dealt with." Minutes went by and it wasn't. The smell got stronger. Two men came into the studio, walked over to the pile of droppings, talked for a couple of minutes over it and then went out. The droppings continued to sit noisomely in the middle of the studio floor. People wandered around with contorted features and handkerchiefs over their noses, regarding the monument to Simba's healthy colonic function from a respectful distance. I asked again for something with which to clear up the mess. No one seemed inclined to listen.

"Now come on," I said loudly, beginning to lose my patience, "all I need is a shovel and I'll do the cleaning up in a trice."

An elegantly dressed girl assistant hurried over to me. "Please, Dr. Taylor, please," she said earnestly, taking my arm, "don't get involved. It's the unions."

"Unions—what unions?" I asked incredulously.

"Well, the question is, which union in the building should be responsible for cleaning up the, er, stuff?"

"But it can be done in less time than it takes to tell. What unions are involved?"

"There's the union that the television centre's normal cleaning staff belong to and there's the quite separate union for the people inside the studio here, the scene shifters and so on."

"And you mean they can't agree who clears up the, er, stuff?"

"No."

"Both unions want the privilege of shovelling that lot?"

"Well, not exactly. You see this type of, well, dirt is extraordinary according to the rule book. It's not only who does the cleaning, but how much extra pay will the chosen ones get."

More folk were now inspecting the mound of excrement which was the centre of the dispute and walking in circles round it, conversing intently. It might have been a suspected bomb. Another girl assistant came in with an air-freshener aerosol and filled the room with the stench of cheap rose perfume. Mixed with the existing odour of lion it made a still more repulsive blend.

"Well, what's going on now?" I growled in disgust.

"They're having a meeting in the corridor outside. Then it will be decided."

Time went by. The girl drifted off. "Oh, look here," I said to the assembled company, without addressing anyone in particular, "if it will ease matters, couldn't I as a paid-up member of the Lion Shitshifters Brotherhood get you off the hook by removing the stuff with a piece of newspaper?"

"'Fraid not, old boy. You're not a member of the right union," replied a voice.

Another ten minutes went by, with Simba's troublemaking offering lying centre stage, before a man came into the studio and announced that the matter had been settled. In just under ten seconds two fellows with dustpans and brushes had the studio floor clear and sparkling.

"Which union won?" I asked the girl assistant.

"The scene shifters. They argued that the, er, stuff should be regarded as a prop, not as ordinary dirt. Eventually that was accepted. The lion, er, stuff was a prop so they shifted it. As it was a prop extraordinaire and could be classed as dirty work in the rule book, they got a bonus."

I wished Shelagh had had a union from which to claim a bonus for all the lion, er, stuff that she had removed from

Simba's convalescent home in the market garden at Rochdale.

There is of course a special satisfaction in helping zoo babies such as Simba, so I was delighted when Katja, one of the Belle Vue chimpanzees, presented Robert the thumb-remover with a daughter. Christened Topaz, this sister for Lee, in whose bed the remains of my pink shirt were still to be seen, had something of her brother's adventurous nature and an apparent interest in race relations! The quarters for the orang-utans and chimpanzees are side by side at Belle Vue, although they are separated by a solid brick wall so the two groups are unable to see one another. At the front of the centrally heated indoor compartments are widely spaced and decorative iron grilles, and outside these there is armoured glass sheeting dividing the animals from the humans and keeping airborne human bugs and viruses at bay. Between the grilles and the glass is a narrow passageway that runs without interruption the length of the house.

Normally baby chimpanzees do not venture far from their mothers, and although we realized that they were small enough to squeeze through the grille at the cage front, we had never known one do so—until Topaz came along. She would run happily in and out of the cage, playing some game such as chasing her shadow and passing between the metal bars with ease. Katja, her mother, did not seem to mind, and the little animal always returned after a few moments' expedition into what for her was the outside world. But one day, as Shelagh and I were standing with Len outside the plate glass watching young Topaz play, she suddenly did something new, something that made us all gasp as we instantly appreciated the possibly serious consequences.

Leaving the chimp cage she moved along the passageway to the left until she found herself for the first time in her life standing outside the living room of the orang-utans. She was fascinated. There through the grille was the great Harold, patriarch and sage of his group, sitting in the middle of the domestic circle with Jane and his other wives tending the orang babies, doing a bit of grooming of their lord and master and sorting through the day's ration of fruit and vegetables which Len had carefully mixed with their wood-wool bedding to set them a sort of treasure hunt to pass the time. The three of us stood in growing apprehension as little Topaz stared goggle-eyed at the covey of chestnut-coloured men of the woods, as their name means in Malay.

Of the three types of great ape, gorilla, chimpanzee and orang-utan, orangs have always been my favourite. They are a peaceable, gentle and tolerant species, and I have become much closer to them than to the saturnine gorillas or mercurial chimps. Nevertheless they can be swiftly vicious and immensely strong if provoked, as when Len had lost a toe and half a shoe to a liverish Harold. It was impossible to predict what might happen to a little foreigner like Topaz who suddenly came upon the scene. Harold and the family had already noticed the visitor waiting without. It was too late for us to do anything like rushing round to the back of the house. We might as well stay where we were, keep our fingers crossed and hope that the young chimp would quickly wander back to Katja before she was set upon as an intruder.

Having gazed at the family group from outside the bars, Topaz apparently found it most inviting, for without more ado she popped through the grille and shuffled up to the mighty Harold with her lips drawn back and her teeth showing in the grin that indicates friendship among chimpanzees. Now for it, I thought. If Harold or one of the females was in a bad mood, little Topaz might be pulled limb from limb before our eyes.

In fact, quite the reverse happened. The baby chimp was accepted into the orang family circle as if she was one of their young daughters who had just come home from school. She took her place at the feet of Harold, who looked down his nose at her and stuck out one index finger, apparently for her to play with. He never moved another muscle. The baby orangs came and sat next to her and solicitously arranged the wood-wool bedding round her bottom to make her more comfortable. Jane half peeled a banana and thrust it into Topaz's face. It was a wonderful spectacle. Here was Uncle Harold playing perfect host and benefactor to his favourite niece from next door; you would not have guessed that he had never before clapped eyes on her. Topaz enjoyed it immensely, and before long was sitting on Uncle Harold's capacious pot belly and gleefully wrapping his long tresses of red hair about her. Harold indulged her like a sultan with one of his numerous offspring.

Shelagh and I stayed watching the touching sight for half an hour. Then we saw Katja come to the grille of the adjoining cage and start chattering anxiously. She could almost have been calling to her infant, "Come on back home now, Topaz. You really can't presume on too much of Uncle Harold's time. Be a good girl and say thank you politely. There will always be another day."

Topaz slid off Harold's belly, put a finger to the lips of the female orangs in a gesture of closeness and went back the way she had come. Katja gathered her up in her arms, far less hairy than those of Uncle Harold, and took her back to father Robert, who does not possess Harold's belly either. Were they saying to her, "Well, tell us all about the folk next door, and did you have a good time?"

So began a delightful association. When Robert and Katja were busy or had had enough of the ever-active chimp, Topaz would slope off and spend a few hours with the neighbours. On at least one occasion she was seen to take Uncle Harold a present of a carrot.

The visiting only stopped when Topaz grew too large to slip between the bars of the grille, but by that time she had other things outside to interest her. Ray Legge liked to take her on his rounds through the zoo and would sometimes let her sit with him in his office when he did his paperwork. She revelled in new places and new faces, and was particularly interested in a group of Arabian camels that had come into quarantine at Belle Vue some months before. They were a sorry sight when they arrived. Every one was thoroughly infested with the microscopic little mite that causes sarcoptic mange, a very common skin disease of camels that is related to human scabies. We began an intensive programme to try to rid the grumpy animals of the troublesome complaint. We sprayed them and dipped them and anointed the bleeding areas each day with soothing creams and ointments, but the mites had burrowed deep into the skin and were protected from chemicals by all the thickening and scaliness they had produced. In the end I decided to bring on the big guns of organo-phosphorus insecticides, helping them to penetrate the layers over the mites by scrubbing off the scales with specially bought yard brushes and hot water.

Topaz accompanied Ray on his many visits to supervise the keepers brushing and scrubbing the insecticides into the camels, and she became familiar with their routine of filling buckets with hot water, adding the chemicals and then applying them vigorously to the bodies and legs of the diseased dromedaries. One day after this had been going on for several weeks an assistant keeper in the great ape house rang Ray's office in a panic. He admitted his fault right away —he had left the door to Topaz's cage open while cleaning it—and now he had to report that the young chimp had disappeared somewhere into the zoo grounds. It was not that she was in any way a dangerous or unpredictable animal, she posed no threat to any child or little old lady that she might meet on her travels, but what might happen if she naïvely paid a visit to the lion compound or the polar bear pit? She might not be as lucky there as she had been with Uncle Harold.

A full search was started, and keepers combed every

section of the zoo from aquarium to elephant house. Eventually Topaz was found. It was the keeper of the camels who sent for Ray to come and collect the fugitive, and quite a sight greeted the zoo director when he went into the camel house. Topaz had obviously been fascinated by all this business of treating the camels, and after escaping from her cage she had gone to their house to help us out with the anti-mange treatment. There she stood, in the middle of a group of camels that towered above her, but which had so far apparently

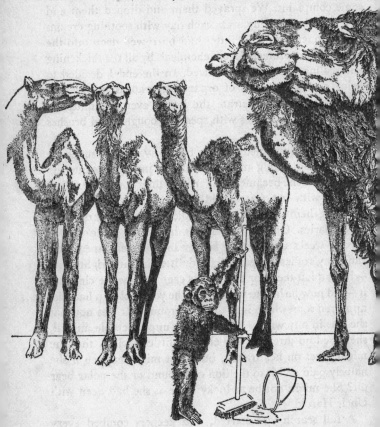

tolerated her presence and had not begun covering her with ejected stomach contents, their normal sign of disapproval. The little ape had decided to give them a good scrubbing down—if the humans were making such heavy weather of it, she would see what a sharp young chimpanzee with muscles and application could do. She had pulled a fire bucket full of water into the thick of the forest of camels' legs and had armed herself with one of the keepers' sweeping brushes.

As Ray and the camel keeper watched, Topaz dipped the brush into the fire bucket and then, constantly displaying the wry grimace of appeasement and keeping up a fussy chatter, which was presumably her way of exhorting the camels to stand still, she scrubbed away at the limbs and the undersurfaces of the bellies all around her. She continued doing this after the humans arrived, pausing only occasionally to look over her shoulder at them as if to assure herself that her efforts to help were not going unnoticed by her superiors. It is hard, wet, repetitive work dressing camels and other hoofed stock for mange, so perhaps one day such chores might be carried out by trained groups of chimpanzee veterinary auxiliaries!

It was not quite the end of the affair when Topaz was safely restored to the great ape house. One week later she began to show signs of itchiness on her arms and chest, and I found that she had broken out in a very fine rash. At first I thought it was an allergic reaction to something she had eaten, but tests showed that she had contracted the mange parasite from the camels. Topaz had scabies. She was not very pleased when it was her turn to be thoroughly lathered and bathed in the special shampoo every few days but, as I told her, picking up such complaints is the sort of thing that a chimpanzee has got to learn to expect when she embarks on a career as a zoo vet.

12

Lee

As if not to be outdone by his sister, Topaz's elder brother Lee was demanding a good deal of my attention at about this time. It was he, resourceful and innovative as ever, who proved to me that at least one hairy little ape, born without pockets and not in the usual run of things issued with a wallet, lunch box or handbag, could give some substance to the ribald fancy about where a monkey keeps his nuts.

I was driving through Belle Vue's grounds on my way home one day after a long session of anointing snakes with a cream to destroy skin parasites when Len, the ape keeper, waved me down. With Len you never knew. Not one to fuss over trifles, he would stroll up and quietly announce the advent of some dire emergency with inexhaustible sangfroid. Matt Kelly would buzz about, crimson-faced, teeth clicking and neck veins bulging like an apoplectic leprechaun, when a crisis broke among the animals, but Len in the same situation would make a Trappist reading his breviary seem like a hysteric. Being flagged down by Len, calm as you please, might mean that all the tigers had literally "gone over the wall" or that the elephant was in difficulty delivering quintuplets.

Winding the car window down, I asked, "What can I do for you, Len?"

"Lee, Dr. Taylor. He's bristling."

Hedgehogs bristle. Porcupines make a fine and flamboyant art of bristling. Dogs when they are in that sort of mood bristle. Chimpanzees do not. Apprehensive, irate or fighting mad, their shiny black hair stays as flat as a pancake.

"Bristling? What do you mean?"

"He's sprouting straw, sort of. His back end. His bottom." Len blinked and scratched his head. "Keeps putting pieces up, er, inside his rectum. Bits of twig too. I just don't know what's got into him. I'm frightened he might do himself some injury."

I got out of the car and walked over to the great ape house with the keeper. Robert leered at me as I went by, and the great Harold, supine in his sunlit seraglio as his womenfolk conducted his toilet, blew a friendly gobbet of saliva in my direction. Lee was sitting on a branch in his open-air quarters, throwing bits of banana skin at pigeons on the edge of the parapet above him. Lee is not a bird-lover and was not good-humouredly feeding the birdies. He was vainly trying to knock one down, a feat which he had achieved at least twice before, using more potent ground-to-air missiles in the form of half-apples.

"See what I mean?" said Len, pointing towards Lee's butt where it hung over the branch. "He's bristling."

Sure enough, Lee's nether portion was sprouting a fistful of stems, stalks and similar bits of vegetation. Pieces of straw and thin twig projected from the chimp's anus, making a stubby corona.

"Are you sure they aren't bits passing through his bowels?" I asked. "Undigested fibrous pieces that he's got jammed?"

"Oh, no. There's no question about it. Lee puts them in there like that. I've watched him at it for more than a week now. Doesn't seem to bother him, but I'm worried he might damage himself internally. Why does he do it, Doctor?"

Why indeed? Lee looked for all the world as if he was growing an embryonic tail. Had he been watching the pigeons so long that he had delusions of one day taking to the air? After fixing himself up with an airworthy straw tail, would he launch himself from the top of his tree one day, long arms flapping wildly, and pursue the pigeons in their own element? A chimpanzee-versus-pigeon dogfight in the sky above the zoo would pull in the crowds on a summer afternoon. Sternly I put such whimsy aside and considered the possibilities. An itchy bottom? Worms?

"Has he been showing any sign of itchiness, Len? Scratching or rubbing himself?"

"No, I don't think so. He seems to select straw and twigs with some care and, well, just hide them there, as if it's a handy place to keep the collection."

My immediate suspicion was that Lee had pinworm itch and was using the straw to scratch the irritating area. "I'll leave you some worming syrup, Len," I said. "It's got a nice fruity flavour which chimps don't usually object to. Dose him with it. If he's got pinworms, that should do the trick. I'll look at him again in a week. With any luck he'll be bristle-free and unadorned by then."

One week later Lee was as healthy as could be. And he still had his tail. If anything it was somewhat denser and more luxuriant.

"He's still got a thatched bottom," said Len blandly. It was true; Lee's posterior had a hint of harvest festival about it, of dying country crafts like straw "dollies" and the ancient custom of well dressing in Derbyshire parishes once visited by the plague.

The other chimps in the house had not copied the fetish, so I decided to see if I could find out more by closer examination. Half an hour after I had slipped a stiff shot of tranquillizer into his mid-morning cup of hot chocolate, Lee was sprawled somnolently in the forked branches of his tree, his eyes glazed and his lower lip drooping. Len and I fished him out of his arbour and turned him upside down. Carefully I pulled the cache of straw stems and twigs out of his rectum, put them to one side and looked inside him with an auriscope, an instrument designed for looking down people's ears but which comes in handy for other more exotic orifices such as dolphins' blowholes and koala bears' pouches. The foreign bodies did not appear to have damaged the lining of the lower bowel, nor was there any sign of parasites or itchy inflammation.

I picked up some of the short straw pieces that Lee had collected and inspected them. Turning them over in my fingers, I discovered something that made my eyes widen. Even Len gave a low whistle of surprise. Lee had not been decorating himself, rooting for parasites or even trying to fly. If anything he had been taking a leaf out of the book of those luckless felons who, until the end of the nineteenth century, were condemned to serve their sentences on French prison ships. Living in the most abominable conditions among murderers, thieves and other desperate characters, they would safeguard their precious personal possessions—a knife blade perhaps, a flint, a needle or a few rolled scraps of paper—in the hollowed-out marrow of a bone. This *plan,* as it was called, was then hidden by being thrust deep into the recesses of the owner's lower colon.

Lee's pieces of straw and twig were his form of *plan* and the booty he was concealing, not from convicts but from a wily bunch of chimpanzee gastronomes, was sunflower seeds. Each day Len provided the apes with a few handfuls of dried sunflower seeds, rich in essential oils and other nutriments. These were especially fancied by the chimpanzees, who would root through their food the moment it arrived, trying to pick out and eat as many of the black and white seeds as they could find. The nimblest and deftest got most. Lee, quite amazingly, had taken matters much further and had provided a unique demonstration of the ability of these advanced primates to use tools.

The straws that lay in the palm of my hand had been split longitudinally. Neatly inserted into the hollow centre of each stem was a row of sunflower seeds. The twigs had not proved as handy. They too had been split at points and seeds pushed in towards the centre but, not being hollow, they had not made such excellent *plans* as the straws. Altogether, Lee had a hoard of sixty-seven sunflower seeds in his little bundle. There was no question of their having got there accidentally; the chimp must have put them there after rations had been issued, no doubt gobbling down as many again at the same time. The ones in the straws and twigs were for a rainy day or at least for a beanfeast in the middle of the night when, with only the peacock's eerie cry breaking the quiet of the sleeping zoo, Lee could stealthily retrieve his haul and nibble happily away in the darkness.

Although Lee's squirrel-like ingenuity was of great scientific interest, it would eventually produce proctitis, an inflammation of the rectum. Reluctantly but firmly I told Len to change all Lee's bedding from straw to wood wool. Twigs, the bark of which contains chemicals important for normal bowel action, were not abandoned, but only ones of too large a diameter to make comfortable *plans* were provided.

Lee ceased to bristle. From watching his unchanged behaviour, his sparkling interest in everything that happens around him and his continued ack-ack barrage against overflying pigeons, one can see no sign that he was once thwarted in his bid to corner the market in sunflower seeds. But sometimes, as I stand and watch him watching me, I wonder. Maybe the gleam in his brown eyes means that Lee knows something that Len and I don't know: that chimpanzees have more than one ingenious way of hiding their treasures.

It was as well that we de-bristled Lee when we did, for a few days later Edith popped her head round my surgery door. "If you don't have any emergencies, you're invited to a party tomorrow," she informed me. "It's a party with a difference, at the Queens Hotel in Manchester. Some charity has organized a pets' luncheon."

"What's that?" I asked her. No one was going to get me tucking into dog biscuits and tinned cat food. Anyway, whose "pet" was I supposed to be?

"Well, the idea apparently is for the diners to be an assorted group of tame animals who will 'bring along' their owners—show-business celebrities and well-known figures in the city. Belle Vue are sending Lee with Len to keep an eye on him. They would like you to go as well." I hesitated, remembering the fiasco of the pets' church service, but Edith went on, "The thing is, it's to raise money for animal charities, so I said you would go."

"OK, Edith," I said resignedly, "book me down tomorrow for a couple of hours' duty as gentleman-in-waiting to a high-living chimpanzee."

When Lee had been younger I had prohibited him and the other baby chimpanzees from going out to children's parties, fêtes and school visits because of the trouble I was having with the measles, colds and upset stomachs they were bringing back to the zoo. Now that Lee was older he was being allowed to attend the occasional function. He enjoyed getting out and about and was especially fond of going with Matt Kelly on some of his evening lecture dates. They invariably ended up after the lecture sharing a glass of beer in a nearby pub, and if Matt was feeling especially generous Lee might occasionally be treated to a glass of his favourite tipple, Advocaat.

Next day I drove to the hotel, one of Manchester's grandest, where already a seething throng of furry, feathery and scaly animals along with attendant personalities, city fathers and press photographers had begun to assemble. There was Lee, neatly dressed, not in the shirt he had stolen from me but in the red and white colours of Manchester United soccer team. He was holding the hand of an obedient and well-behaved Len. On a large dining table at one end of the room, feeding bowls and dishes and stainless steel trays had been prepared and filled with appropriate food for each of the animals according to a large seating plan which had been pinned up on the wall. There would be sunflower seeds for the parrots (I hoped Lee would not spot them first), fruit salad for the primates, meat and biscuits for the dogs and raw liver for the cats. There was a place but no actual food for each of the reptiles, as they were not thought likely to fancy lunch under such circumstances. By each plate or bowl was a container full of water. Although chairs had been provided for the dogs and the chimpanzees, there were also high stools for the smaller monkeys and perches for the birds. The idea was that the doting owners would stand behind their pets, watching as the Noah's Ark chomped away to the pop of flashbulbs and the whirr of cameras.

I located a gin and tonic and stood in a quiet corner, admiring the kaleidoscope of the animal kingdom before me. A movie actress with a pair of petite squirrel monkeys that she had borrowed from a photographer for the occasion stood sipping cocktails in speechless horror as the little creatures did unmentionable things on her mink stole, a portly alderman slopped martini down his waistcoat as the dalmatian on the other end of the leash he held lunged menacingly at a passing parrot, and a fruit bat brought along by a local disc jockey got itself frantically entangled in the hair of a waitress who was moving round the humans with a tray of canapés. The fruit bat had not been looking where it was going because it was fleeing the beady-eyed attention of a brace of hawks sitting unhooded on the gloved hands of a guest dressed up like Robin Hood. It was this incident which led to the trouble and to my becoming involved.

The waitress, terrorized by what she thought was a day-light attack by a vampire bat fancying a nibble at her scalp, dropped her silver tray and scattered the appetizing morsels all over the carpet. All hell broke loose, as dogs and monkeys, bush babies and macaws, all no doubt with empty stomachs in preparation for the famous luncheon, thought with one accord that this was it and scrambled, scurried or fluttered about the floor gathering up bits of smoked salmon on toast, stuffed olives, wedges of salami on pumpernickel and cubes of savoury cheese. There are inevitable consequences when a mean and hungry parrot descending on a tasty titbit of shrimp wrapped in cucumber finds himself eyeball to eyeball with a Yorkshire terrier, all tassels and bows and lacquered toenails and dying for a bite

to eat, or when a pet goat, noted for always having her own way, is holding one end of a stick of celery while the other is grasped meaningfully by a muscle-bound Rhesus monkey in a sailor suit. The din was deafening: birds screeching and protesting, dogs barking, felines of various species spitting and hissing, monkeys howling and humans shouting and screaming.

Worse was to follow when, the canapés having been devoured, the animals began to look at one another with an eye to starting the main course. A swirling, screeching, colourful mêlée of fur and feather began to develop in and out of the legs of the distraught owners. Women wept as their dear Tiddles or immaculately groomed Fido disappeared gleefully into the scrum, glasses were knocked from hands by swooping birds and, worst of all, leads, chains, leashes and halters of every kind became tangled and intertwined round chairs, pinstripe trousers, high-heeled shoes and potted palms. Things worsened as a City Councillor was swept neatly off his feet, his ankles lassoed by strands of leather and chain link. Having been brought low, the worthy gentleman had to endure being crossed and recrossed by the paws and claws of the rioting beasts as they struggled to free themselves from the tangle.

To the noise and confusion another horror was now added. A man from a pet shop had come along with his twelve-foot python. At the outbreak of hostilities this non-venomous reptile had weighed up the situation, decided to adopt a neutral stance and, having extricated itself from the grip of its owner, made off across the floor to the relative quiet and peace to be found beneath some seating round the walls. Under the seating ran a line of central heating pipes, and around these the python wrapped itself, no doubt to observe the proceedings from the safety of a grandstand seat. The pet shop owner, pursuing his errant snake, got down on his hands and knees and started to extricate it from the piping. It is not an easy job with an animal of this size: just as you unwind and hold one part of the snake, another part is winding itself even more firmly into a tight hold. The owner tugged and tugged and the more he tugged the more the python resisted and increased its coils on the piping. Then, as his master's attempts to winkle him out became ever more desperate, the snake became somewhat alarmed. Like most other creatures, when snakes are alarmed they tend to lose control of their bowels, and very soon the dining room of this rather superior hotel was filled with the indescribable and unmistakable stench of upset python. Few of those present could have smelt such an odour before, but the glazing of their eyes and contortion of their facial muscles showed that none of them would ever forget the experience.

Meanwhile, the big dining table which had been specially laid out for the feeding of the animal guests was standing completely neglected. Its centrepiece was a large iced cake containing only sponge and sugar, which was thought to be acceptable to most of the birds and animals invited. Crowning the cake was a representation of the Manchester coat of arms in red and gold plastic. The public relations people had visualized the Lord Mayor cutting the cake and handing out slices to everyone from pekingese to parrot. Dining table and iced cake were deserted and forgotten as the skirmishes over the spilled canapés raged on. I was fully occupied trying to avoid getting bitten whilst acting as umpire and interposing portions of my anatomy between the contenders in the bouts around me. Len was clutching Lee's hand but the chimp, adopting a superior air as if such hooliganism was beneath him, waited calmly on the fringes of the battleground, stooping only to pluck the odd tail feather from a mynah bird or macaw if it came within reach. But his stomach was beginning to rumble as the canapé hunt reached its climax; still not a peanut nor a potato chip, not a cocktail onion nor a gherkin had passed his lips. Then he spotted the big iced cake. Invitingly unattended it stood, and the look of it appealed most powerfully to Lee's sweet tooth. Without attracting too much fuss, he slipped his hand from Len's and sidled over to the dining table.

Lee was actually up on the table sampling the icing with both hands before Len realized that his companion was no longer by his side. "Lee! Come off there this minute!" he shouted, pushing his way through the battlefield as fast as he could.

Lee may not have heard him above the hullabaloo, but he certainly gave no sign of obeying. He dug his hard black nails deep into the succulent sponge and scooped out a sweet mouthful.

Len's approach was hampered by an irate ferret clinging tenaciously onto his ankle. "Dr. Taylor, it's Lee! Grab him!" he roared, hopping on one leg and trying to unpick his dogged assailant.

I looked up, saw the looter at work on the table and decided to let my two canine opponents in one particularly bitter three-cornered match sort it out between themselves. There were still a lot of furious bodies between me and the chimpanzee.

Lee summed up the situation like lightning and realized that Len's expression was not only one of anguish at the needle-like teeth perforating his lower limb, but also meant the imminent confiscation of what was turning out to be a very tasty cake indeed. There was only one thing to be done. Picking up the whole cake on its wooden stand, Lee cleared off to look for a quiet spot where he could continue his lunch away from all these bothersome beasts. Out of the dining room, along the corridor, down the stairs went the small chimpanzee with the wounded-looking cake carried effortlessly on one shoulder. Looking back briefly, he saw us in full pursuit, accompanied by a very angry catering manager. Lee reached the lobby still without having spotted a suitable hideaway where he could hole up and do the cake justice. Visitors coming into the hotel stood dumbfounded as the little midget waiter, obviously some strange foreign immigrant on the hotel staff, scurried by with his short order. Some room service! A bellboy, arms outstretched, gallantly tried to halt the cake's progress. For his pains he was spat accurately in the eye as the chimp swerved by with all the skill of one of the international half-backs in the team whose colours he was wearing.

At last Lee found the ideal place, or so it seemed. An open door led into the gentlemen's washroom. Glancing back once again to check that his pursuers were not too close, chimpanzee and cake disappeared inside and closed the door. Cautiously I opened the door and went into the washroom, followed by Len and the catering manager. There was no sign of Lee, nor for that matter of anyone else. We were faced by a row of toilet cubicles, all with closed doors. Now we had a delicate problem. Behind which door was Lee? I decided to leave it up to the catering manager—at least he was a member of the hotel staff. Miserably this poor fellow went from cubicle to cubicle tapping on each door and inquiring in diffident tones, "Excuse me, we've lost a chimpanzee. Could you please answer so that we know he's not in there?" A succession of oaths and other sounds of indignation produced by obviously human occupants floated back over the top of the cubicles.

Eventually we came to a cubicle the door of which was firmly shut, but where the "engaged" sign was not showing at the lock. "Er, anyone in there?" called the catering manager. "Sorry to disturb you if there is."

No answer came. Lee had been run to earth, and when Len shinned up the side of the cubicle and looked over the top, there was the chimpanzee sitting happily on the toilet seat with the cake in his lap and his legs wedged firmly against the door to keep it closed.

Len prepared to descend on Lee and what was left of his meal just as the chimpanzee was sucking icing from the little plastic coat of arms which he had removed from the cake and was using as a sort of spoon. When Lee saw that the game was nearly up he took one last frantic scoop of cake and packed it, together with the coat of arms, into his mouth. Down dropped Len, Lee made a futile jump to try to escape, the remains of the cake fell into the lavatory pan and it was all over. Carried out of the cubicle by determined hands, and with his cheeks bulging with cake, Lee gulped the final mouthful, forgetting in the heat of the moment that the little plastic coat of arms was also in his mouth. An instant later he was coughing and choking. Len had seen him take the piece of plastic and we immediately realized what had happened: it was jammed somewhere at the back of his throat.

"Quick, slap him hard on the back while I hold him upside down!" I shouted, hoisting Lee up by his ankles with both hands and letting his head dangle close to the floor.

Len slapped and slapped at the hairy black body and Lee coughed and groaned but no plastic coat of arms appeared. The chimpanzee was becoming markedly distressed; the mischievous escapade was turning into something much more grave. I laid the ape down on a chair in the washroom and sent Len to my car for my bag. Anxiously I looked into Lee's familiar face and saw that his gums and lips were already turning slightly blue. His breathing was hideously noisy and laboured. All his vital energy seemed suddenly drained out of him. He had neither the spirit nor the power to resist as I opened his jaws wide and probed over the back of his tongue with my fingers. I could feel nothing abnormal. Len came dashing back with my bag and I pulled out my stethoscope. Normally Lee objected to this instrument—he seemed as frightened by the rubber tubes as he was by a plastic or rubber toy snake—and given half a chance he would pick the head of the stethoscope off his skin and puncture the sound-receiving diaphragm with his teeth, but now there was no objection as I listened to his straining chest wall. What I heard confirmed that the chimp was just not getting enough air into his lungs. The plastic decoration for the cake was stuck somewhere in his airway.

Wedging one hand between his teeth, a hazardous position in a conscious ape were he not in such a critical state, with the other I pulled his lilac-tinged tongue as far forward as possible. Len shone my pencil torch down the throat for me. I could see Lee's tonsils and larynx very clearly. Across the opening to the windpipe was an arrow-shaped splinter of red plastic, a tiny piece of the coat of arms but enough where it was lodged to threaten to asphyxiate the chimpanzee at any moment.

Still using one hand as a mouth gag, I took a pair of long artery forceps from my bag and, with Len lighting the way, reached into the depths of Lee's throat with the metal jaws. The shard of red plastic fluttered with each in-and-out of the chimp's agonized breathing. Please God don't let it drop down the dark red hole into the trachea! I reached it and with a gasp of relief clamped the forceps firmly round it. Out it came. Lee began to breathe more easily but still far from normally. Most of the coat of arms was still missing. I looked down the throat again as Lee gurgled and his lilac-coloured parts began to regain a little of their healthier, salmon-pink tinge.

Where was the rest of the cursed cake decoration? It was surely too big to have actually gone down the windpipe. Then a terrible thought occurred to me. If Lee had split one piece off the plastic, perhaps he had crushed the remainder into a dozen smaller fragments, now sucked far beyond my reach into the bronchial tubes. Ice water ran down my spine as I imagined the consequences: chest surgery far beyond my experience in zoo animals. There was just one other place where the bigger part of the plastic might have lodged: above the soft palate. Suppose Lee had almost swallowed the coat of arms and then blown it up again by coughing when the splinter had broken off and wedged in his larynx. It could have been shot forward into the space at the back of the nose and above the roof of the mouth. Perhaps it was there, jammed between his adenoids. To look up and round the back of his soft palate I would need a mirror of the kind used by dental surgeons or something long and shiny which could be bent at the end.

"Please ask at the cocktail bar if they have any stainless steel plungers for mixing drinks," I said to the catering manager. One of those might do. If I could only see the smallest flash of red or gold for an instant I would know its whereabouts.

Lee was by this stage much improved, although still breathing noisily and with effort. Part of his airway was still obstructed: the thought of bits of plastic in the lung continued to haunt me. When the catering manager returned he was carrying a variety of plungers of differing lengths for my inspection. I selected one and then asked Len to hold the mouth open again while the catering manager was reluctantly pressed into doing something that catering managers do not normally do in smart hotels—putting a full nelson wrestler's hold on a now restless chimpanzee. With the chimp's breathing still embarrassed I was loath to give any form of anaesthetic which might depress his respiration still further.

Shining my light down the mouth, I passed the plunger between the tonsils and past the tip of the soft palate. The plunger's circular base was now in a position to reflect back up into the recesses behind the nostrils. Directing the beam of my torch onto the plunger, I moved the two instruments about, trying to bounce light off anything that might be hidden out of my sight. Suddenly I saw a hazy splash of red reflected in the stainless steel of the cocktail plunger. I wiggled the plunger and saw some more red and then a fuzzy flash of gold. It was there! The coat of arms was lodged above the soft palate.

As long as I could keep Lee breathing via the mouth, I should have time to get him to my surgery, where I could use special instruments to remove the plastic, but first I decided to try something that only works occasionally. Sitting the miserable little thief upright in his chair, I slapped him hard and abruptly on the forehead. His head flew back and he looked at me with an expression of surprise and reproach. Nothing happened. Again I slapped him hard between the eyes and the little head flew back onto the hairy shoulders. Lee gave a retch, coughed once and there was a tinkle as he spat a lump of red and gold plastic onto the washroom floor. When I matched it with the fragment that I had extracted with my forceps it fitted perfectly; the ornament was complete, not a scrap of plastic was missing.

Immediately Lee's breathing became normal and the strange noises disappeared. He was feeling more himself, for he back-kicked the catering manager in the solar plexus, winding him and forcing him to release his grip. Manchester's heraldic escutcheon had been saved, and Lee went home to Belle Vue somewhat chastened by his experience but with a stomach fuller than most of the other animals invited to the ill-fated luncheon. For some reason they have not held such an event since.

When I arrived home there was the delicious aroma of one of Shelagh's fish pies, the treat of the week made from cod, cheese and dry white wine. I rather fancied a large helping of that with mashed potatoes after the interrupted and rather insubstantial nibblings at the Queens Hotel.

"You'll never believe what happened with Lee today," I said cheerfully, slipping off my coat. "I'll tell you all about it while I'm getting some of that inside me."

"You won't, I'm afraid," Shelagh replied, darting into the cloakroom and unhooking her coat. "You're off back to Belle Vue. There's just been a call from Ray. He's got two polar bear cubs. And I'm coming with you!"

Good-bye, fish pie! Of course, it was December. I had known that Crystal, the female polar bear, was once again near her time. Ray must have heard the cubs squeaking and used the anaesthetic dart that we had had on stand-by as planned. And now it sounded as if he had successfully cub-napped a pair of twins!

If there was one of the frequent police radar traps on the Manchester road it would just be hard luck. I was going to get to Belle Vue in record time. If I was nabbed I would have a fine excuse, and if they did not swallow my story it would be worth a fine and an endorsement on my licence to get my hands on my first newborn, warm and squirming, snow-white polar cubs.

"What did Ray say?" I asked as I gunned the Citroën out of Rochdale.

"That things didn't look good at all," replied Shelagh.

My heart plummeted. I wish I had a jet helicopter, I thought. No doubt every household will have one by the year 2000, but here I am with twelve miles of road to cover and every vehicle in front of me seemingly being driven in the middle of the road, at a snail's pace, by an opium-eater.

Ray and the twin cubs were in the dispensary when we charged into the zoo. "I'm afraid it's too late," he said as we went through the door. His face was haggard with disappointment. Matt Kelly stood silently by. Two plump, grubby little bodies lay inert on the table. Newborn all right, but quite definitely not warm, squirming or snow-white.

"What happened?" I asked as I opened the miniature jaws and looked at the pallid gums.

"The keeper didn't notice anything until he heard her scratching away at her bedding. Then he thought he heard a faint squeak. I darted her straightaway and we went in. We found she'd cleared all her straw away from one corner, down to the bare concrete, and had pushed the cubs there. They were probably born this morning. When I got to them they were cold, damp and not moving. Still attached to their placentas. She'd neglected them again."

Unstimulated by the tongue-licking and warmth that their mother should have provided, and left untended on the hard floor, the cubs had slipped into hypothermia. I picked one cub up in each hand and squeezed their chests firmly and rhythmically. I tried to feel an arterial pulse—nothing. They were floppy and chill and they had the familiar look of death about them.

"Get some hot water," I said. "From the tap will do. As hot as a good hot bath. Quick. In a bucket or anything."

Matt Kelly had the water ready in seconds. I plunged both cubs in, immersing their whole bodies except for their little muzzles. Underwater I continued squeezing and massaging their chests. "Shelagh, you do one while I do the other." I passed the manipulation of one of the babies over to her. "Pump rhythmically but don't dig your finger ends in too viciously," I instructed. I had seen lungs ruptured and heart muscles haemorrhaged many times where over-enthusiastic artificial respiration had been applied to tiny creatures.

Minutes went by and suddenly Shelagh yelled, "Mine's moving!"

I looked at its mouth; it was definitely much pinker. I told her to keep pumping and I struggled on with mine. "More hot water, Matt," I said. He topped the bucket up. Then I too felt it. My cub was moving slightly. It was not quite so floppy. There was a faint muscular tension growing in the furry lump within my clasping hands.

"Both out!" I said. "Stethoscope!" I listened to the two now warm little cubs. Dab-dab, dab-dab. I heard the faint soft heart sound in one. I turned to the other. Dab-dab, dab-dab. "They're alive!" I shouted. "Back in the water, keep respirating!"

There was no doubt now, both cubs were wriggling their bodies under water. "Right, out again!" I said. "I'll take them both." I held both cubs by their back halves, one in each hand at arm's length. Then I whirled my arms round and round in fast, wide circles. I hoped the centrifugal force would throw out any mucus blocking the cubs' windpipes. Then it was back into the hot water. The cubs were

struggling manfully now but there was not a squeak out of
their little throats. "Out again! We'll try mouth-to-mouth."

Again Shelagh took one cub while I handled the other.
Sticking the cubs' snouts into our mouths we blew gently
but firmly. The minute chests expanded. We pulled out the
snouts and let them expire our air. We waited. Moments
passed. They were not breathing automatically. More
mouth-to-mouth. And more. Puff in, squeeze out. The twins
were developing the healthy feel of coiled wire springs in our

hands. We stopped and waited again. The pink mouths opened a fraction, two stubby pink tongues tentatively probed the outside world and then, giving me an exhilarating "high" surely greater than any experienced by a main-lining junkie, they both voluntarily breathed strong and deep.

Shelagh cheered, Matt and Ray shouted in delight and I laughed and laughed. I picked up the cubs and turned them over onto their backs on my palms, a good test for vigour in the newborn. Cussedly they squirmed themselves round into the head-up, belly-down position which self-respecting little critters prefer. An excellent response, and as a bonus they voiced their protest at being so peremptorily upended and emitted their first, glorious squeaks of complaint. I have never seen Shelagh so thrilled.

Within minutes we began dripping a solution of pre-digested protein and glucose into the twins' mouths by way of a feeding bottle designed for premature human babies. The cubs were installed in an infra-red heated box, where they scrabbled and wriggled and grumbled lustily. I had no intention of going home until I had seen them do one more thing: start to suckle. The protein and glucose solution was ideal as a first-aid source of energy, but after that it was going to be all the way to weaning on tinned Carnation milk.

"Come on, Shelagh," said Ray when he had prepared the first milk feed, "you must have the first honour." He gave her the two little feeding bottles.

On tenterhooks we watched as she proffered the rubber teats to the two protesting cubs. Then there was silence. The twins had grabbed the teats hungrily and contentedly begun to draw in the milk.

It was now up to Ray and Matt to organize a two-hourly feeding schedule round the clock. It would be worth it. Bears grow very quickly and these little fellows were never to look back.

"Come on, Shelagh," I said after scrubbing up and going out to the car, "bugger the fish pie. Let's go and have a bottle of champagne at the pub."

13

"Everything Marvellousest"

The little old blind lady in Singapore's Lion City Hotel stamped her enthusiastic way up and down my back in bare feet, grinding her heels into every one of my ill-humoured vertebrae and accompanying each audible rending of my bones with a triumphant, high-pitched "Atcha!"

I was on my way back from Bangkok, the cesspool of unscrupulous animal dealing, where I had been to check a collection of beasts being offered for sale by Thai traders. Not only had the job meant Norman's wrath about yet another absence from the practice, it had been a depressing experience in itself. In noisome, unlit dungeons, I had run my hands over baby elephants as knobbly as blackberries with multiple skin abscesses and had gingerly pulled one live, tick-covered king cobra out of a stinking pile of forty of its long-dead fellows. I had seen giant bird-eating spiders that had died from thirst—they need liquid refreshment in hot countries just as much as the trappers who sell them for one cent and the dealers who buy them for retail at five dollars—and had discovered that even after death the reddish hair that covers their fearsome limbs can cause painful inflammation. I had also been knocked about while taking blood samples from a bunch of anaemic-looking water buffaloes. Slipping while drawing blood from the jugular of one animal, I had suddenly found myself with my nose in the mud and both hands protecting the back of my head as a dozen buffaloes milled round and over me.

Now, along with my bruises, I was in Singapore to spend a few days exploring this most kaleidoscopic of Asian islands and to recuperate from my "buffalo-ing". The ancient Chinese masseuse had done wonders in erasing the buffalo footprints, but she had beaten, .drummed, kneaded and trodden copious quantities of oil of wintergreen into me. I could not scrub away the all-pervading mentholated smell, and for days after her ministrations I was as pungent as a bottle of smelling salts. When I was invited by Feng Lo, a rich Chinese importer of lapis lazuli, to visit his private menagerie of exotic animals, I arrived at his bungalow close to the famous Tiger Balm gardens with as much animal appeal as camphor has for moths.

The pride of Mr. Feng's collection were his four Hartmann's mountain zebras. Fine, plump animals in a shady corral in his back garden, they were as tame as donkeys, he told me; his nephew had actually sat on the stallion's back. The zebras trotted over pleasantly enough when Mr. Feng called them. They nibbled the sugar lumps he offered, then they looked at me and sniffed me over. A vapour rub in human form—ugh! Ears went back. The whites of their eyes flashed. Soft nostrils wrinkled and snorted. The three zebra mares spun petulantly away, but just to show how he felt the stallion lunged and bit me neatly and painfully right on the tip of my nose. Stung by spider hairs, trodden by water buffaloes, smelling like a throat lozenge and now this! Mr. Feng hopped from foot to foot in a frenzy of apologies, but as I clamped a padded handkerchief to my bleeding nose and watched the stallion fling up his tail and canter arrogantly away my attention was riveted. One of his testes was grossly abnormal, about five times the size of the other. I pointed it out to Mr. Feng.

"What could it be, Dr. Taylor?" he inquired, looking troubled.

"It could be a hernia or it could be a tumour. Whichever it is, an operation is called for without delay. If it's a growth it should be removed, and a scrotal hernia must be repaired before it strangulates a piece of intestine."

Mr. Feng scratched his head and sucked the bean-sized solitaire diamond on his right index finger. "But who can do it here in Singapore? The vets here know riding horses. But zebras?" He muttered quietly to himself in Chinese. Then he suddenly smiled and prodded me in the solar plexus. "Ha!" he said cheerfully, as if it was now perfectly clear to him. "No problem. You will do it, Doctor. What a good idea!"

"But I . . ." I began. Neither hernia nor tumour demanded instruments more complicated than those I always carry in my emergency pack, but the anaesthetic—that was the problem. I could buy barbiturates on the island, but they would be useless unless shot straight into a vein, hardly practical on a fighting, kicking zebra stallion. Chloral hydrate solution in the drinking water might work, but the stuff tastes so appallingly bitter that an animal will go for two or three days before, maddened with thirst, it drinks the knock-out drops; I had never used the method, feeling it to be slightly barbaric. I had phencyclidine, but no phencyclidine ever again in zebras for me after the dreadful night at Belle Vue when I had first tried it on the species. What I needed was etorphine or xylazine, both excellent drugs for zebras. There was not a drop of either in Singapore.

Then I remembered my motto, "Always say yes". In danger of extinction in its native mountains of Damaraland, South-West Africa, this precious creature was not likely to come my way very often. And it needed help. This maxim, of accepting opportunities positively in the knowledge that in almost every case there is time later to change one's mind if absolutely necessary, has paid off time and time again in my career. To be sure of being "in" is better than to risk being "out" through timidity or indecision. It stirs the blood, brings far fewer disasters than might be expected and should be heartily recommended to all except young ladies and, so they say, members of the armed forces. Quick affirmative decisions are like ice-cold champagne after a cloying meal, clearing the palate of the mind.

"Right, Mr. Feng," I said briskly, "I'll do it. I want your

men to build a stout wooden crate for the zebra, the sort you might use to transport him. No holes in the sides, absolutely solid. But with no top on."

"It will be done by tomorrow," he replied. "Anything else you want?"

"Yes. A bottle of chloroform and the address of a good, quick tailor, the sort that runs up suits for tourists in twenty-four hours."

"Ah, yes." Mr. Feng looked faintly perplexed. "For you, of course. You want a suit?"

"No," I said, grinning, "for the zebra."

While Mr. Feng, clearly puzzled by my sudden attention to the zebra's sartorial welfare, set about organizing the crate building, a taxi took me to an address he had given me. It dropped me in the old Chinese quarter at the fringe of a large crowd watching the weaving dragons and warbling, white-faced maidens of a street opera. Gongs boomed, cymbals clashed, villainous landlords were revealed and demons machinated as I pushed my way through the rapt audience into the cool gloom of the tailor's little shop.

"I want you to make something unusual," I told the tailor, a young man with long vertical moustachioes and a Pink Floyd T-shirt. "By tomorrow, or better still tonight. For a zebra. Yes, zebra. Ze-bra. Z-e-b-r-a. Horse, black and white. Stripes." Pencil and paper were produced and I sketched what I needed.

Chloroform was a veteran method of anaesthesia and I had never used it in my life on a large animal. But I had watched horses knocked out by it while I was at university, and now I needed a mask of the sort I had seen being used there. A simple strap round the back of the animal's ears kept in place a canvas cylinder divided into two compartments; the horse's muzzle fitted into the upper one and the smaller lower one held a wad of cotton wool soaked in chloroform. A small hole between upper and lower compartments allowed air to be drawn through the cotton wool in the lower chamber into the upper chamber and so into the respiratory system of the animal.

"But I have no canvas," explained the tailor.

"Then use some of the firmest felt material you have, the sort you put inside collars and lapels of suits."

The tailor caught on quickly. It would be ready at five o'clock and would cost twenty . . . well, what about fifteen . . . OK but at eight you are getting it at cost price . . . well, agreed then at five dollars.

As I drove back to the Lion City Hotel to do repairs to my nose, I recalled with a shudder the last time I had seen a chloroform mask fitted to an equine. A final-year student, I had watched a hunter mare rear in the air at the first whiff of gas, snatch the halter rope from the groom and spin stiffly backwards through 180 degrees to crash with the back of her skull on the ground. Since then I had stuck purely to injectable anaesthetics. But chloroform was what I was going to have to use, and on a rare and unknown quantity. I wondered what Mr. Feng would have said if I had announced that I was literally starting to practise on his beloved zebra.

The mask was ready as promised at five o'clock and the tailor had made a very creditable job of it. It seemed strong enough, and had the silk square normally sewn inside jacket linings attached to the muzzle compartment: "Jerome Hua—Tailors of Singapore—By Appointment to Dukes and Kings since the Tenth Century and Mr. Rocky Marciano." "The World's One and Only Zebra Tailor" would have had even more panache, I thought.

Since the zebras lived completely outdoors with trees for shade and no kind of stable, I had decided to operate in the cool of the next day, just after dawn. Before turning in early, I strolled through the alleyways round Bugis Street taking in the aromas, colours and sounds that swirled in the soft evening air. Little boys scurried round with steaming buckets of rice. Hand-held firecrackers with a report like a hand grenade exploded showers of paper streamers over the shabby roofs. Pretty girls in cheongsams split limes by pulling them down taut thread and squeezed the juice over heaped half-moons of watermelon. At one stall a boy was passing sugar cane through an iron mangle and collecting the sweet, refreshing juice in jugs of ice. Stopping for a glass, I washed down a couple of painkillers to pacify my muscles, which were grumbling about water buffaloes once again.

As I stood drinking, I saw that the next stall specialized in cubes of some sort of meat, speared onto fine wooden skewers and coated with a spicy satay-nut sauce. The skinned little creatures from which the stallholder was cutting the meat were not immediately recognizable. Curious, I wandered over. Not rabbits or cats—knowledge of the subtle differences between those two carcasses once heads, feet and skins have been removed had come in useful when the Rochdale police were prosecuting a rogue of a market trader who went out at night nabbing stray toms for sale the next morning as "fresh meadow-trapped bunnies". Encouraged by my apparent interest, the stallholder pulled my sleeve and pointed to the back of his stall. Hanging there upside down, with its clawed feet lashed to a rickety cross-pole, was a live Malayan flying fox, or fruit bat.

"Him very fresh. You like me kill him? Roast quick. Taste very good fresh." The man smiled a solid gold smile and pulled my sleeve again. The furry brown creature's wings were bound tightly with thread that had cut into the flesh and was crusted with dried black blood. There were holes in the shining soft fabric of the wing membranes, like moth holes in cotton curtains.

"How much for him?" I asked.

"Six dollar. But I fry him good. You like." He grabbed a meat cleaver. "Him very good with plenty soy."

"I'll have him," I said, taking off my shirt. "Wrap him in this."

The man looked flabbergasted. Then he dazzled me with the eighteen-carat palisade of dentures again. "Ah! You take home. You know how cook? You got good wife cook?"

"Yes," I replied, "I know how to deal with him." I paid my six dollars, snipped the thread and cord binding the animal and wrapped him carefully in my shirt with just the tip of his nose protruding.

"Good appetite, sir," bade the stallholder as I went off in search of a taxi.

Back at the Lion City I took the squeaking bundle to my room and carefully unwrapped him in the bathroom. The cords had cut deep and his wings were showing as much daylight when fully extended as a slice of Emmentaler cheese. It was tricky working single-handed; Malayan fruit-eating bats are up to a foot long and can nip severely if mishandled. Slowly I managed to clean up and treat his wounds, and for good measure I gave him a shot of long-acting penicillin. When I released him he managed to flutter up to the shower curtain and grab hold, upside down. From there he watched me with glinting, angry eyes. Out of the hotel I went again and from the street stalls which bustle merrily all night long I bought a selection of peaches, cherries, mangoes and bananas. I distributed the fruit along the bottom of the bath, used the bidet as a rather inefficient sort of upside-down shower and went to bed.

As usual before a major operation I lay in bed worrying about all the complications which might beset my treatment of the zebra the next day. Singapore nights are humid enough without the sweats such thoughts provoke. At least I found next morning that the flying fox had been down to eat some of the fruit and was now dozing comfortably, hanging from the edge of the lavatory cistern.

Sticking the "Do not disturb" card on my room door, I went off as soon as the sky was light to begin operations at Mr. Feng's bungalow. Everything was well prepared. The stallion had been lured into the crate and was now securely fastened. Keeping a wary eye on the other three zebras and on their companions in the paddock, a pair of large ostriches and three brindled gnus, I climbed up the wooden side of the container and looked down at my patient. He glared up at me, ears back, and bucked with an irate squeal.

Normally the chloroform mask is put on a horse first and, once it is secure, the anaesthetic is introduced into the lower compartment. But I might have only one chance of getting near the head of the creature before all hell broke loose, so I had decided to put the chloroform-soaked swab in the felt mask before touching gloves with my adversary. Having done so, I climbed back up the side of the crate with the loaded mask in my left hand. The zebra was standing below and across me with his head to my left. Gently I tapped him on his bristly mane with my right hand. He threw his head up and tried in vain to get his teeth into me; the crate was just narrow enough to stop him bringing his head round. Quick as a flash I plunged the mask over his muzzle with my left hand and leaned way down with my right to bring the retaining strap over his ears. He bellowed like a bull, crashed, thrashed, kicked and tried to spring vertically upwards on all four legs.

The edge of the crate cut into my stomach as, red in the face, I leaned down into the container and clung grimly on. Suddenly the stallion reared, his forelegs scrabbling at the wood in front of him, and I felt the retaining strap of the mask slide crisply over his poll. Then, as the beast descended once again onto all fours, his weight combined with my desperate grip on the strap flipped me in the twinkling of an eye down into the crate. To Mr. Feng and his men standing anxiously round the crate, one instant I was there, the next I had vanished. The crate now contained one irate stallion zebra, its muzzle enveloped in a fuming bespoke felt mask, and one veterinarian sitting side-saddle on the zebra's back, red-faced and winded. If the crate door had been opened at that moment, there would have rocketed out a duo that would have given the crowd at any rodeo the spectacle of a lifetime.

The zebra was still. So was I. Maybe, I thought, I can sit here until he goes under, like a cowboy having his horse shot from under him in slow motion. If I stood up I might slip down between my patient and the crate walls, or my movements might excite him again. All went well for a few moments, until the spinning world and the strange, overwhelming smell in his nostrils sent a wave of fear through the stallion's growing drowsiness. He made one final, instinctive explosion of effort. First crouching slightly and then powerfully extending his legs, he produced the buck of all bucks. For Mr. Feng and his men the earlier disappearing trick cleverly reversed itself. One moment there was just a box; the next a veterinarian rose like a malfunctioning Minuteman out of its silo and flopped in an awkward heap on the hard edge of the crate.

This spectacular double act produced a fresh crop of bruises round my midriff. Painfully I climbed down and sat on the ground, listening to the zebra's protests die away as the anaesthetic took good hold.

"My goodness!" exclaimed Mr. Feng as I panted and puffed and longed for the little old lady with the oil of wintergreen. "That was most spectacular, Doctor. I can see you have done that many thousands of times."

"Yes," I replied. Liar.

The sun was just beginning to pour a thread of molten gold along the horizon of the South China Sea, and tall grey pillars of cloud dotted the sky like poplars. There was no sound from the crate. I climbed up again. The stallion was down, unconscious. I poked him with my toe. No reaction. "Right, open the front of the crate," I shouted. "Pull him out as quick as you can."

Six Chinese dragged the patient out and I began my examination of the enlarged testis. One feel was enough. No hernia this, but a tumour. The whole organ was hard and irregularly shaped. Probably a non-malignant growth, but it had to be removed. The other testis seemed normal and the animal's ability to breed would not be affected. After checking his heart and lungs, adjusting the mask and telling one of Feng's men to make sure that none of the other animals in the enclosure interfered with my little field hospital, I washed and sterilized the operation site. That done, I made one incision, withdrew the diseased testis and tied off its massive blood supply with thick catgut in a special non-slip knot. To make doubly sure that there would be no disastrous haemorrhage once the beast was up and running, I placed a second similar ligature and then cut the testis free. As I would have done with a horse, I left the incision in the scrotum so that it could drain easily but packed the empty space where the testis had lain with a fly-repellent antibiotic powder. It was done. I took the mask off and after fifteen minutes the stallion groggily regained his feet and walked slowly off towards his mares.

"Now," I said to Mr. Feng, "let's see what sort of growth it was."

I knelt on the ground and sliced open the mass with my scalpel as Feng and his men crowded round. There was a distinct "ping" as my blade struck something hard as flint in the centre of the testis. I opened the incision with my fingers and the Chinese men gave one loud gasp of amazement. Out from the middle of the swollen organ fell a shining white object the size of a matchbox. There was no doubt what it was: a perfect zebra's molar tooth. It lay in the palm of my hand, complete with roots, glinting enamel and roughened cusps.

"A dragon's tooth!" exclaimed one man, gingerly extending a grubby hand and touching the object with the tip of one finger as if it might leap up and gnaw him.

"What beast is it that carries teeth in his loins?" murmured another reverently, spitting on the ground.

There was a babble of excited Chinese debate. One man

saw the mark of the demons in the affair, another thought that if the English veterinarian had not been so foolish as to interfere the stallion would have sired the Chinese version of a centaur. The oldest man, Feng's gardener, claimed that the tooth should be planted at once, for perhaps this was the strange seed of which Lao-Tse, the venerable philosopher, had written and which might grow into the Tree of Knowledge.

Mr. Feng himself roared with laughter as he pulled his wallet from his hip pocket, extracted four or five notes and, flicking his lighter into flame, set fire to them. As the paper money curled and blackened into fragile ash he blew the fragments into the air with a puff of breath and another burst of laughter. "What fortune, Doctor!" he cried. "What fortune! You know what that is. You know. Oh, what fortune!"

Yes, I knew what it was, but during all the commotion I had not been able to get a word in edgeways. It was a tooth that had got lost. When the embryo zebra was a microscopic ball lying in the womb of its mother, the cells of which it was composed had started to sort themselves out. Those cells that were to become the brain and spinal cord took up their positions, kidney cells fell into line over here, liver cells got into a huddle over there, heart cells gathered at a point that would one day be the centre of the chest cavity and so on. During all this sorting out of a thousand and one different kinds of cell, some got lost, just like groups of schoolchildren making their way to their allotted coaches at the end of a school outing. This is how some kinds of non-malignant tumour develop, why bone tumours can grow in kidneys or, as in this case, teeth can bud in testes. Once a tooth cell, always a tooth cell. Magic? Yes: nature's magic.

Before I could try to outline this fascinating faux pas of embryology to the exultant Mr. Feng, I had the distinct impression that the sky had fallen in. A split second before, I had been watching Mr. Feng prove inexplicably that he had money to burn. Wham! Now I was flat on the ground, my nose buried for the second time in a week in material more suitable for doing good to rosebushes. Worse, I was being thoroughly stomped on by heavy, clumping, scaly feet with iron-hard toenails. I was being gone over by an ostrich. The man detailed to keep an eye on the other animals in the paddock had left his post in the excitement of finding the tooth, and the male red-neck ostrich had decided to come looking for trouble. Now, beak gaping, ragged wings flailing in victory, he did his war dance on me. I could not help noticing that he lacked both the restraint and the skill of the little old lady and that instead of oil of wintergreen he used slimy white droppings. Stoically, hands once again covering my head, I took my beating until the ungainly bird was shooed away. As I climbed wearily to my feet I wondered whether the animal kingdom had put a contract out on me; there seemed to be no shortage of creatures from buffalo to zebra to ostrich that were bent on doing me in.

"You must stay for breakfast, Doctor," said my host, helping me to his bungalow. "I must discuss with you the good fortune you have brought me."

I began to feel the bruises on my bruises easing a little as a servant brought rice, eggs and lightly cooked vegetables to a lapis lazuli table. We drank the most delicate of pale jasmine teas with petals floating on the surface. "Tell me, Mr. Feng," I asked, "why did you burn the dollar bills?"

The Chinaman lit a cigarette and smiled. "Because of the tooth, of course," he said. "By the way, please pass it to me."

I pulled the tooth out of my pocket. I had hoped to keep it as a curio, a souvenir of the operation, but it was obvious from the way Mr. Feng lovingly turned it over in his fingers and then locked it in a bureau encrusted with lapis lazuli that he considered it well and truly his. His zebra, his zebra's testis, his miraculous tooth.

"The burning of the money was a traditional custom, a

polite thank-you to the spirits of my ancestors. One must not forget the old courtesies, Dr. Taylor, even in these days of television and atom bombs." Mr. Feng still had not explained what he had to be so grateful to his ancestors about.

"The tooth is what pathologists call a 'foetal rest,' a tissue that was displaced during . . ." I began to describe the nature of the object. Mr. Feng waved a slim finger at me.

"Quite, quite," he interrupted, "but I think you do not understand how Chinese culture looks at such things. For a tooth to grow in the organ of generation, the source of life and potency, such a conjunction has profound implications. I could feel the energy of it when I touched it. I cannot describe what its abilities, its qualities must be, are."

"But you don't believe in magic, surely?"

He smiled benignly and looked at me over his spectacles. "What is magic? Today's science is yesterday's magic. There are powers that we Chinese understood when Western peoples were barbarians in wolf skins. Those powers existed then, they exist now. They are our heritage, the wisdom of the Middle Kingdom. Acupuncture, herbs—only now does the West begin to sniff round things our ancestors knew centuries ago."

"Well, what are you going to do with the tooth?"

"Quite frankly, Dr. Taylor, it will make me a millionaire."

"How on earth . . .?"

"I estimate it weighs, oh, forty-five or fifty grammes. Do you realize how much a Chinese with the necessary resources and need will pay for just a little of that tooth, say a milligramme or two, when it has been carefully ground into a fine powder? No? I tell you. At least one hundred and fifty pounds sterling! The power of my zebra's tooth is love, my dear Doctor, love."

I had operated on a zebra with a pathological testis and presented my client with an aphrodisiac, the raw stuff of love philtres that would rake in a fortune from oriental gentlemen who were long in loot but short in amatory abilities. I gulped and thought of the hundreds of horse teeth lying neglected in the mud round the slaughter-house in Rochdale.

"Believe me," Feng continued, "when Tok Man in Medan hears about my zebra tooth, he will willingly pay five hundred dollars for some dust from it. He is a terribly worried man. A beautiful wife for ten years now and no sign of a child. You know, he has a sea cow in his garden just so that . . ."

My ears pricked up and I interrupted quickly. "Sea cow, Mr. Feng? He has a sea cow?"

"Yes, as I was saying, he has a sea cow caught by the fishermen. Now there is an animal that can turn a man into a lusty young lover again."

"How?" I asked, my attention riveted. Surely by a sea cow he meant a dugong, the strange vegetarian creature that started the mermaid myth.

"By collecting its tears, Doctor. The Indonesians say that a few drops from its eyes have never been known to fail."

Mr. Feng described the Medan sea cow; it certainly sounded like a dugong, a harmless, totally aquatic mammal that grazes on underwater weeds and grasses. The Australians had considered the possibility of farming the beasts, for the flesh is said to be utterly delicious. I had seen their cousins, the manatees, in Florida and California, but had never set eyes on a dugong.

"I would like to see this sea cow if possible," I said. "Is Medan very far?"

"An hour by jet. I will telephone Tok Man and I will give you the air ticket; after all, Doctor, today you have made me a millionaire." He went to the bureau and returned with a blue disc of lapis lazuli, bound with gold and with a rampant gold dragon in the centre. "And this is for you. The dragon will bring you luck."

It would take two days for me to obtain a visa so that I could fly out to Medan on the north-east coast of Sumatra, and I decided to see if I could pass them peacefully consuming gin slings in the bar at the Raffles Hotel and acquainting my taste buds with the unique (and as it turned out unexciting and wildly expensive) savour of shark fin and bird's-nest soup. With a bit of luck, hidden away in the fleshpots, I would avoid being stamped on by a yak or savaged by a tiger that had heard of the beastly conspiracy to do me in.

But the moment I arrived at the Lion City I was promptly thrown out. The hotel manager met me in the foyer with my bill and a pale and angry face. Apparently, ignoring my "Do not disturb" card, a maid had gone in to clean my room and on opening the door to the bathroom had been "attacked by a vampire bat". The maid had been given several large brandies and the day off, and the rest of the staff were threatening to walk out if the monster was not exterminated. The hall porter was crouched outside my bathroom door with a .22 rifle, hoping to shoot the bat through the keyhole. The manager had given strict instructions that on no account was the door to be opened, which made it pretty difficult for the gun-toting porter.

I paid my bill, bought a Pan Am flight bag to pack the flying fox in, cleaned up the bathroom and, feeling a bit like Count Dracula revealed, marched out of the hotel with all eyes upon me. I decided next to smuggle my companion into the Singapore Hyatt. After checking in, I set up my "vampire" once again in his private and now rather plushier bathroom and dressed his wounds for the second time. Although it might seem pointless when thousands of his fellows are being slaughtered or exploited at the need or whim of human beings, I still feel it is worthwhile to wrestle with the problems of one individual creature. An animal deserves attention for its own sake. That is another reason why zoo work satisfies me rather than the mass medicine of poultry or fish farming.

All the same, I had a problem with my adopted fruit bat.

I did not like the look of the small Singapore Zoo, and I could not take him with me when I left in a couple of days. For thirty-six hours I worked hard at anointing and injecting his wounds while he consumed peaches and mangoes and made quite a mess of the Hyatt's marble bathroom. On my last evening in Singapore I packed him back into the Pan Am bag and took a ferry across the straits to Malaysia. At the dockside I hired a taxi and told the driver to take me inland to the first bit of dense forest. Once there I walked through the long grass into the trees, loaded a syringe with one more dose of long-acting penicillin and squatted down. The flying fox had his last jab, looked at me, squeaked and then launched himself out of the unzipped bag, up and away. Unsteadily he flew into the canopy of dark green and disappeared. I hope he made out. I walked straight back to the surprised taxi driver and told him to take me back to the boat. Strange fellow, this Englishman, I could see him thinking. All that way just to relieve himself!

Back at the hotel I rang Norman Whittle to report on my progress and to check that all was well at home. "I'm in the thick of the love potion business," I said, "and I'm off to Indonesia in the morning to see a mermaid!"

The intercontinental cable hissed for a few seconds as Norman digested my remarks. "Look, David," he said finally, "I don't understand a word of what you're saying. If you're lying drunk in some oriental bath house while I'm up to my ears tuberculin testing all Farmer Crawshaw's Friesians, covered in mud and muck with it raining non-stop for six days, we're going to have a little chat when and if you ever get home." He put the receiver down.

I went out specially then and there and bought a coloured postcard of a Chinese girl in traditional Cantonese dress. It was the sort of card which if tilted slightly revealed the girl naked and unadorned. I sent it to Norman bearing the words, "Best wishes from the bath house. Hic!"

Next day I flew into Medan, a sprawling, seedy town of sleepy streets with houses stripped to the bare wood by the scorching sun, clouds of eye-stinging dust bowled along before a hot wind, and garish, squeaky trishaws. An enormous bald Chinese gentleman with the figure of a Japanese sumo wrestler, a purple shirt and candy-striped trousers was waiting by his car to meet me. "Welcome to Medan," said Tok Man.

We drove for twenty minutes before Tok Man pulled up

beside a high wooden fence set in a grove of dense hibiscus bushes. It surrounded a compound set in rustling fields of tobacco and backed by a broad strip of yellow sand, with the dark grey ocean beyond. Through a heavily padlocked gate we entered a cool shaded yard with a bare earthen floor surrounded by hutches, cages and a variety of wooden boxes.

"I have only a few animals I keep for my . . . personal use," said Tok Man. "Feng Lo tells me you are interested in seeing my sea cow. Come, I will show you."

He led the way to a large coffin-like box in one corner of the yard. It had a stout grille set in the top. Looking in I could see the ungainly shape of a real-life mermaid, a dark brown, helpless roly-poly with dried and cracking skin and eyes that were caked and sore. It was a dugong all right and in terrible shape.

"Why do you keep it so?" I asked in dismay. "These are rare and precious creatures which need water; you see what is happening to the skin."

"Yes, indeed, they are precious, Doctor. Oh, how wonderful it would be if I could get more tears from the beast! Believe me I have tried, I have laboured, but I cannot make it weep."

I could hardly believe my ears. "But . . . " I faltered.

"You see, Doctor," interrupted the fat man, "if I can speak in confidence, I am a man in my prime with a wife who is a true jewel, but"—his voice hushed—"I have no children. It is a matter of great sadness and embarrassment to me. I have tried many things, and always I refuse to lose hope, but I remain . . . how do you say?"

"Impotent," I said.

He nodded glumly. "So now I try the creatures I have here."

"What exactly do you do?" I inquired, grimly fascinated.

He pointed to the various containers around us. "Over there I keep a bunch of snakes. Every day I slit the gall bladder of one and run its bile into a glass of wine. I think perhaps it will help."

"And the sea cow?"

Tok Man sighed. "Each morning I beat it with a bamboo in the hope of making it weep. But so far I have collected no tears. If only I could. Sea cow's tears are most potent." His face brightened. "Doctor, perhaps you can show me some trick of making it weep?"

I pinched myself to make sure that I was not lying in bed at home having a surreal nightmare. The pinch stung but I did not wake up. "It would be best if you released the sea cow," I said as steadily as I could. "I know no way of producing tears." In actual fact I did have a chemical, carbamylcholine, which I had used to increase the tear flow from crocodiles, but I was having no part of this sick affair.

"Ah well," said the Chinaman, "I suppose I must press on with the beating. It eats nothing and I must get some tears before it dies."

"Give it some lettuce and spray it with water," I said, grinding my teeth fit to shatter them as we left the compound, but I do not think he was listening.

I went back to the hotel in Medan where Tok Man had found me a room, but could think of nothing except the sad plight of the dugong. I had to do something, but what?

There was only one thing for it. At eleven o'clock I walked out of the hotel carrying just a little money and my small bag of surgical instruments, found a trishaw and with much difficulty explained to the driver where I wanted to go. By trial and error we came eventually to the compound in the hibiscus grove. Motioning the nonplussed fellow to stand against the high fence, I hoisted myself up on his skinny shoulders and pulled myself over the top. The moon was full and seemed to fill half the sky as I dropped down into the yard. No guard dogs, just a squadron or two of mosquitoes and the friendly carolling of tropical frogs.

The first thing I did was to prowl round the fence, looking for a way out. A shimmer of silvery water and a foul stench led me to a slimy ditch running under the fence towards the seashore. I went over to the dugong's box. It was too dark to see much inside it, but I could hear its soft breathing. I felt round the grille. It was secured by two bolted hinges and a piece of thick, twisted wire. A dog barked in the distance as a vehicle rumbled by. I tried not to think how Indonesian jails might appear to a European found guilty of burglary, but cold sweat ran down my forehead and stung my eyes.

With a pair of artery forceps from my bag I began to unravel the stout wire. Off it came, and a moment later I had lifted the grille and was stroking my first mermaid. This was no time for the finer points of animal handling. I pushed the horizontal coffin over onto its side and with a blubbery plop the dugong fell out onto the ground. Off I went round the compound again, until I found a length of sacking. Folded lengthways several times, this made a strip to put round the base of the dugong's paddle-like tail. "Come on, old chap," I whispered as I slipped the sacking round its quivering body, "this is no time to stand on ceremony."

I began to pull the 200-pound beast backwards over the rough, dry ground. It was back-breaking work and I knew that I must have been scuffing the skin on its underside. After what seemed like an hour, with muscles indignant at my adding yet further insult to injury, I reached the murky ditch. Dismally I realized that I would have to go down into the slimy water and drag my mermaid with me through the hole in the fence. The mosquitoes had a field day as I slithered and strained first one way and then the other, basting myself thoroughly with ooze, algae and creepy-crawlies. At last I was through the fence. Sweat soaked my hair as I pulled the dugong through after me.

Next came a prickly ploughing through a stretch of reeds. I lost a shoe. Tiny bats skimmed silently across the moon. I cowered at every sound, expecting at any moment to be discovered. Then, mercifully, I heard the first soft hissing of the sea smoothing the sand. Stopping at the edge of the shore to rest, I sat down beside the dugong and put an arm round it. All animals like a cuddle, and I might never get this chance again. I touched the strange soft muzzle and delicate lips. Its gums were warm and velvety, its breath grassy like a cow's.

Then I was up and off again, down the gently sloping beach to the water's edge. At last I could remove the sacking and throw it into the black water. The dugong could smell the ocean and was restlessly moving its head from side to side. Wearily I bent down and rolled it over and over like a giant sausage until the surf caught it and the water bore it off the sand. Its crusty, flaking back was caught by the creamy moonlight as it orientated itself, floated on the surface for a second and then, with a wave of its paddle, dived beneath the foam. It was gone. Tired, wet and smelling like a compost heap, I trudged round the edge of the hibiscus grove and slapped my gaping trishaw driver on the back. "Back to the hotel," I said, gave him every rupiah note I had in my pocket and threw my one remaining shoe into the gutter.

Tok Man arrived in the hotel lobby next day with bad news. Vandals had broken into his compound and stolen his sea cow. "Some people will eat anything," he fretted. "And my wife is scolding me more than ever. She doesn't seem to realize I want children as much as her. It's a curse on me. Today I will slit the galls of ten live snakes and drink their bile with wine."

I should have released the snakes as well, I thought, but he would easily have got some more. Perhaps . . . I decided to give him some advice.

"Look, Mr. Tok," I said, "I work with wild animals and, though I do not talk about it usually, I do know of one substance which, if taken very carefully—not too little, not too much—can produce an effect a thousand times stronger than snake bile or sea cow's tears. It always works. If I let you have some of this drug for your personal use, will you promise not to let it fall into the wrong hands?"

For a moment I thought the corpulent fellow was going to kiss me. "Of course, certainly, yes, yes, *yes*!" he gurgled. "How much do you want for it?"

"Nothing," I replied. "It is unprofessional and unethical for me to supply you with it. I do it only as a favour."

Tok Man was beside himself. I went up to my room and opened a tin of orange, sugar-coated vitamin B tablets. Counting out one hundred, I put them into an envelope and went back downstairs.

"Now, take one tablet at exactly eight o'clock in the morning and one tablet at nine o'clock at night," I instructed. "They always work, without fail. But you must not mix them with anything else. No snake bile, no sea cow's tears. They must be allowed to work alone."

Tok Man looked at the envelope he was clutching as if it was a bag of fine black pearls. "Doctor," he exclaimed, grabbing my hand and shaking it furiously, "I cannot thank you enough." He thanked me all the way to the airport and kept shouting his thanks as I went through the departure gate.

Well, I thought, if he believes what I say hard enough, those harmless little vitamin pills will do their stuff, a lot of poor reptiles will be spared being gutted alive, Mr. Tok will not need to replace his truant sea cow and the only loser will be Mr. Feng, who will have one less customer for his ground-down zebra's tooth. And that was how it turned out, for two months later, back in England, I was to receive a cable from Tok Man in Sumatra: DEAR DOCTOR WONDERFUL. EVERYTHING MARVELLOUSEST. WIFE VERY MUCH PREGNANT.

But now, as I flew between the cloud stacks suspended over the Malacca Straits, I looked down and wondered how the dugong was faring and whether it was at that moment gorging its empty belly on succulent bunches of submarine sea grass. I thought of a fruit bat and a zebra stallion and then of the cats, dogs and cattle that I might have been busy with at that very moment in the familiar streets and fields half a world away. Safe and comfortable respectability in Rochdale, or challenge and fulfilment? Mr. Tok's dugong or Mrs. Partridge's arthritic corgi?

The decision was taken as the plane touched down again at Singapore Airport. As soon as I got home I would make my peace with Norman Whittle and break the news. I was going to take the plunge and set up my own practice to work only with wild animals from now on. There was no going back.